BLOCKBUSTERS QUIZ BOOK 6

This book adaptation of *Blockbusters*, the very
successful Central television series game, can be
used in one of two ways. By yourself you can
solve the clues as you would a crossword puzzle,
writing the answers in the spaces provided and
shading or colouring in the hexagons; or, you can
play it as a game with friends, one being the
quizmaster and two being competitors, one trying
to get a linking pattern of hexagons across and
one down.

Whether you solve the clues yourself, or with
friends, you'll have hours of amusement and have
masses of information at your fingertips.

Also in the Blockbusters series in Sphere Books:

Blockbusters
Quiz Book 6

Based on the Central Independent Television series produced in association with Mark Goodson and Talbot Television Ltd

SPHERE BOOKS LIMITED

Sphere Books Limited, 27 Wrights Lane, London W8 5TZ

First published in Great Britain by Sphere Books Ltd 1987
Copyright © 1987 by Sphere Books Ltd
Central logo copyright © 1982
Central Television programmes © 1983, 1984, 1985, 1986, 1987
Central Independent Television plc.

Blockbusters Quiz Book 6 compiled by Bill Garnett

Sphere Books claim full responsibility for the questions
and answers in this volume and every effort has been made
to ensure their accuracy.

TRADE
MARK

Set in Times

Printed and bound in Great Britain by
Cox & Wyman Ltd., Reading, Berks.

Blockbusters
Quiz Book 6

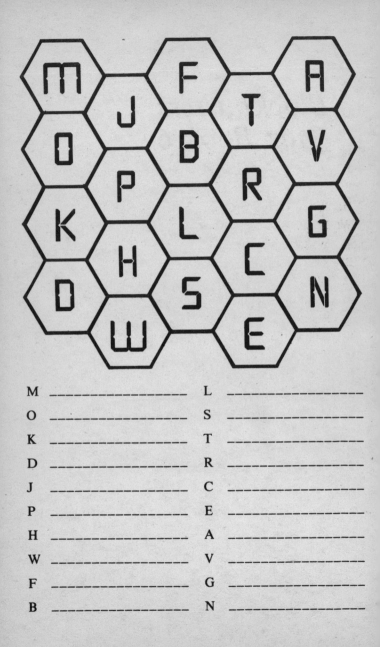

M _____	L _____
O _____	S _____
K _____	T _____
D _____	R _____
J _____	C _____
P _____	E _____
H _____	A _____
W _____	V _____
F _____	G _____
B _____	N _____

M: What 'M' is pie topping made from egg whites?

O: What 'O' is someone the wrong side of a rugby ball?

K: What 'K' is a New Zealander?

D: What 'D' is a triangle-shaped Greek letter?

J: What 'J' was the star of the first talking film?

P: What 'P' is anarchic rock music?

H: What 'H' is a cigar and a city?

W: What 'W' is a poetic word for anger?

F: What 'F' is a setter's tail?

B: What 'B' is to decapitate?

L: What 'L' was a Hungarian pianist and composer?

S: What 'S' is leather with a napped surface?

T: What 'T' comes before tone, step and time?

R: What 'R' is a tedious routine?

C: What 'C' is the 'Windy City'?

E: What 'E' is the manner in which you speak?

A: What 'A' is a rocket and a god?

V: What 'V' is a long, open porch?

G: What 'G' is the degree a road slopes?

N: What 'N' was an arc-builder?

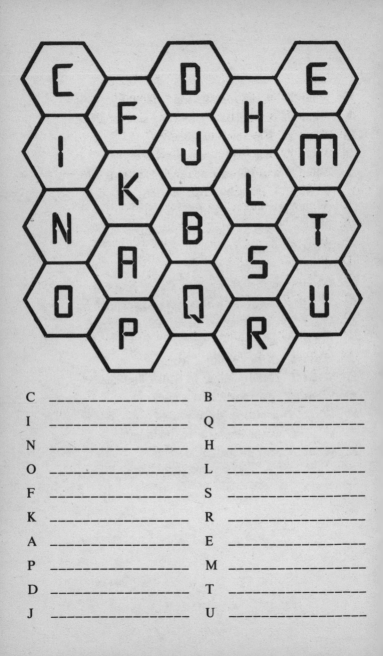

C	_____	B	_____
I	_____	Q	_____
N	_____	H	_____
O	_____	L	_____
F	_____	S	_____
K	_____	R	_____
A	_____	E	_____
P	_____	M	_____
D	_____	T	_____
J	_____	U	_____

C: What 'C' is 'The Garden of England'?

I: What 'I' is slightly ill?

N: What 'N' is a small metal spike?

O: What 'O' is a dish made of eggs?

F: What 'F' comes before pipe, tank and pump – or can be eaten?

K: What 'K' is West German chancellor?

A: What 'A' is a flowering shrub plant?

P: What 'P' is a specialist in child medicine?

D: What 'D' is a rheostat light switch?

J: What 'J' was the god of beginnings?

B: What 'B' is the thicker end of anything?

Q: What 'Q' is an idiosyncracy?

H: What 'H' are ladies' tights and stockings?

L: What 'L' is a Scottish lake?

S: What 'S' is a device used to inject fluid?

R: What 'R' is the 'Eternal City'?

E: What 'E' is an obsolete measure of forty-five inches?

M: What 'M' is a sauce eaten with lamb?

T: What 'T' is a woman's skirt trail – and a locomotive?

U: What 'U' is a capacity for understanding?

G _____ I _____

Y _____ L _____

A _____ P _____

T _____ O _____

V _____ H _____

S _____ F _____

U _____ D _____

B _____ M _____

E _____ J _____

N _____ R _____

G: What 'G' is a ravine (with a gold deposit)?

Y: What 'Y' is 0.9144 of a metre?

A: What 'A' is the French singer of 'She'?

T: What 'T' is a froglike amphibian?

V: What 'V' is a wine-based, herb-flavoured drink?

S: What 'S' is a country bordering Lebanon?

U: What 'U' comes before state, done and age?

B: What 'B' is a small tool for hole-making?

E: What 'E' is an ambassador's residence?

N: What 'N' is to catch or apprehend?

I: What 'I' is the Oxford University magazine?

L: What 'L' was 1987 world darts champion?

P: What 'P' is a duck dish and a city?

O: What 'O' is a cinematic award?

H: What 'H' is a polite way of saying 'Hell!'

F: What 'F' means frantically angry?

D: What 'D' is the two at dice – and forty-all at tennis?

M: What 'M' is a derogatory term for a small dog?

J: What 'J' is the tool used to lift a car?

R: What 'R' was syncopated piano music?

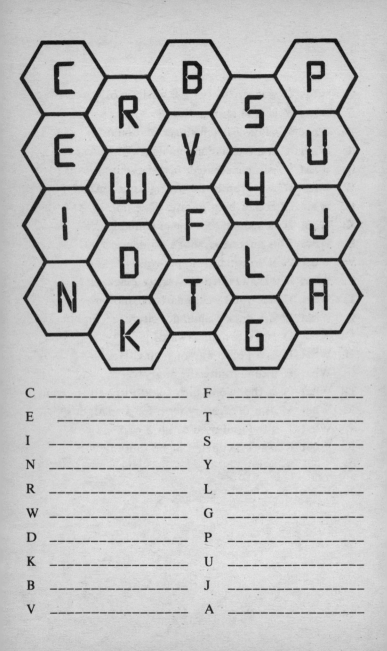

C _____ F _____

E _____ T _____

I _____ S _____

N _____ Y _____

R _____ L _____

W _____ G _____

D _____ P _____

K _____ U _____

B _____ J _____

V _____ A _____

C: What 'C' was the star of the western *High Noon*?

E: What 'E' is part of an atom?

I: What 'I' is burnt at religious ceremonies?

N: What 'N' is an island and province of Canada?

R: What 'R' is the traditional Sunday joint?

W: What 'W' is a Red Indian hut made of skins?

D: What 'D' is a drill or stupid student?

K: What 'K' comes before ring, word and hole?

B: What 'B' is a monkey with a dog-like snout?

V: What 'V' is a railway station – and a cross?

F: What 'F' was the last dictator of Spain?

T: What 'T' is a traditional mender of pots and pans?

S: What 'S' are a group of people who combine to do business?

Y: What 'Y' is a quick, sharp bark?

L: What 'L' is the fifth sign of the Zodiac?

G: What 'G' is pregnancy?

P: What 'P' is the smallest South American republic?

U: What 'U' are representatives of workers' rights?

J: What 'J' was a ragtime composer and pianist?

A: What 'A' is the imaginary line round which something rotates?

F _____
O _____
K _____
R _____
T _____
A _____
E _____
B _____
P _____
D _____

N _____
J _____
S _____
H _____
U _____
G _____
M _____
W _____
C _____
L _____

F: What 'F' was a female US jazz singer?

O: What 'O' is a method of photographic book reproduction?

K: What 'K' is a tailless arboreal Australian marsupial?

R: What 'R' comes before cast, shod and house?

T: What 'T' is a Spanish city famous for sword-making?

A: What 'A' is a self-evident truth?

E: What 'E' is Mayor of Carmel?

B: What 'B' is a platform projecting from a house?

P: What 'P' is to supplicate the Almighty?

D: What 'D' is a 'wet' person?

N: What 'N' comes before born, gate and market?

J: What 'J' is a large rally of boy scouts?

S: What 'S' is the outline of a story?

H: What 'H' means Henry?

U: What 'U' is a Manchester football team?

G: What 'G' is rough voiced or mannered?

M: What 'M' were the original people of New Zealand?

W: What 'W' is a container for money?

C: What 'C' is to gently entice or wheedle?

L: What 'L' are British Rail almost always?

M _____	L _____
O _____	S _____
K _____	T _____
D _____	R _____
J _____	C _____
P _____	E _____
H _____	A _____
W _____	V _____
F _____	G _____
B _____	N _____

M: What 'M' was star of the film *Paint Your Wagon*?

O: What 'O' are hops stored in?

K: What 'K' is a type of cabbage with open curled leaves?

D: What 'D' means to toy amorously?

J: What 'J' is a disease that turns skin yellow?

P: What 'P' is the port of Athens?

H: What 'H' comes before Ford – and after Rex?

W: What 'W' is a small kangaroo?

F: What 'F' is traditional music?

B: What 'B' is a Spanish golfer?

L: What 'L' is rubbish and puppies born together?

S: What 'S' is water saturated with sugar?

T: What 'T' is a native of Central Asia east of the Caspian?

R: What 'R' is the sound of dry leaves?

C: What 'C' is a poisonous hooded snake?

E: What 'E' is to abscond with a lover?

A: What 'A' means for a short time?

V: What 'V' is a solemn promise?

G: What 'G' is to dig in the ground?

N: What 'N' is one's lowest point?

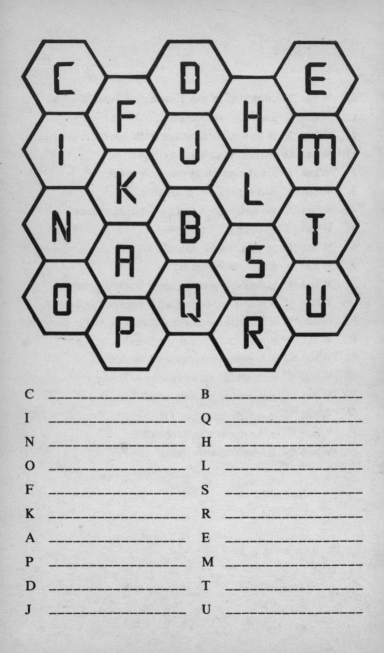

C	_____	B	_____
I	_____	Q	_____
N	_____	H	_____
O	_____	L	_____
F	_____	S	_____
K	_____	R	_____
A	_____	E	_____
P	_____	M	_____
D	_____	T	_____
J	_____	U	_____

C: What 'C' comes after black, pea and wood?

I: What 'I' is a Spanish romantic ballad singer?

N: What 'N' is to steal – or arrest?

O: What 'O' is the noise of a pig?

F: What 'F' is fitness, condition or trim?

K: What 'K' is a South African gold coin?

A: What 'A' is flushed with, or washed by, waves?

P: What 'P' is a prickly rodent?

D: What 'D' is government by the people?

J: What 'J' is an old Irish dance?

B: What 'B' means commonplace or trivial?

Q: What 'Q' was a 'swinging sixties' fashion designer?

H: What 'H' is a large piece or person?

L: What 'L' is a country bordering Vietnam?

S: What 'S' is a formal ecclesiastical meeting?

R: What 'R' is someone who shows no pity or compassion?

E: What 'E' is to omit a vowel in pronounciation?

M: What 'M' is sheep meat?

T: What 'T' is Australia's smallest state?

U: What 'U' is a sense of injury or offence?

G _____   I _____

Y _____   L _____

A _____   P _____

T _____   O _____

V _____   H _____

S _____   F _____

U _____   D _____

B _____   M _____

E _____   J _____

N _____   R _____

G: What 'G' is Britain's third largest city?

Y: What 'Y' is a light pleasure vessel?

A: What 'A' means uncle-like?

T: What 'T' is to twirl your thumb?

V: What 'V' is the sixth sign of the Zodiac?

S: What 'S' is the TV personality who can fix it for you?

U: What 'U' is a persistent open sore?

B: What 'B' comes before gage, man and pipe?

E: What 'E' are atoms called when energised?

N: What 'N' is a British military canteen?

I: What 'I' means beginning?

L: What 'L' is Australian slang for hooligan?

P: What 'P' is a promenade concert?

O: What 'O' is extremely fat?

H: What 'H' was a UK defence minister who resigned?

F: What 'F' are surgical pincers?

D: What 'D' is where milk is processed?

M: What 'M' was the soul sound from Detroit?

J: What 'J' is a woman of stately beauty?

R: What 'R' is a crisp, rebaked piece of bread?

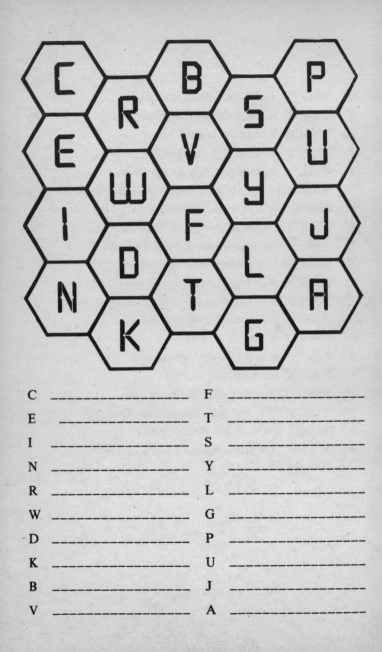

C _____   F _____

E _____   FT _____

I _____   S _____

N _____   Y _____

R _____   L _____

W _____   G _____

D _____   P _____

K _____   U _____

B _____   J _____

V _____   A _____

9

C: What 'C' is a high fashion designer?

E: What 'E' is the resister in an electric kettle?

I: What 'I' is to bring upon oneself?

N: What 'N' is pile, a racing tip and a short sleep?

R: What 'R' comes before peck, grass and whisky?

W: What 'W' is headquarters of *The Times* newspaper group?

D: What 'D' is someone who gives blood?

K: What 'K' is Barbie Doll's boyfriend?

B: What 'B' is a method of secret voting?

V: What 'V' was Roman god of fire and metal-working?

F: What 'F' is a place where a river can be waded?

T: What 'T' is slang for someone silly?

S: What 'S' is cohabitation of different life-forms?

Y: What 'Y' is a major Japanese sea-port?

L: What 'L' is to stagger?

G: What 'G' is a moorland game bird?

P: What 'P' is a case for keeping loose paper or drawings?

U: What 'U' is an ideally perfect place?

J: What 'J' is a type of gold club?

A: What 'A' is clumsy, bungling or embarrassing?

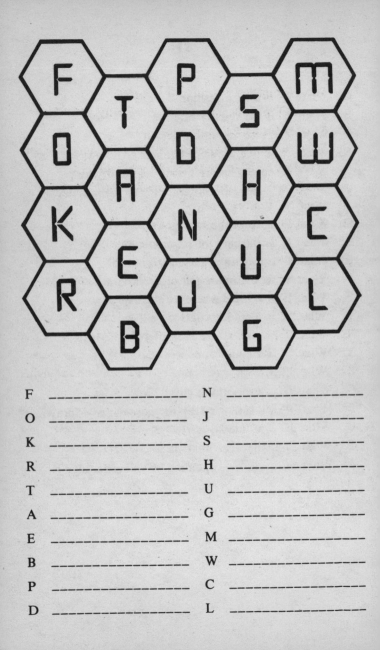

F _____   N _____

O _____   J _____

K _____   S _____

R _____   H _____

T _____   U _____

A _____   G _____

E _____   M _____

B _____   W _____

P _____   C _____

D _____   L _____

F: What 'F' means of iron?

O: What 'O' was the singer of 'Love Really Hurts'?

K: What 'K' is an Eskimo canoe?

R: What 'R' comes before hour and candle, and after gold?

T: What 'T' is called the 'roof of the world'?

A: What 'A' is the first sign of the Zodiac?

E: What 'E' is a piece of live wood in a dying fire?

B: What 'B' comes before holiday, teller and note?

P: What 'P' comes before able, hole and folio?

D: What 'D' means to do with the home?

N: What 'N' is a housing for an aircraft engine?

J: What 'J' was a Roman poet and stoic?

S: What 'S' is a stick to flatten fizzy drinks?

H: What 'H' is dull or commonplace?

U: What 'U' is being out of work?

G: What 'G' is a stringed instrument played with the hands?

M: What 'M' is something purely fictitious?

W: What 'W' is world heavyweight boxing champion?

C: What 'C' is criminal or blameworthy?

L: What 'L' is Australian slang for flashily dressed?

M _____ L _____

O _____ S _____

K _____ T _____

D _____ R _____

J _____ C _____

P _____ E _____

H _____ A _____

W _____ V _____

F _____ G _____

B _____ N _____

M: What 'M' is to increase in number?

O: What 'O' were a pop-singing family?

K: What 'K' is a fine cotton used as cushion filling?

D: What 'D' is a northern English county?

J: What 'J' is a wine bottle eight times normal size?

P: What 'P' is the left hand side of a boat?

H: What 'H' is meek and modest and rhymes with a bee?

W: What 'W' is a derogatory US name for illegal immigrants?

F: What 'F' is a fat Shakespearean figure of fun?

B: What 'B' comes before side, hand and bone?

L: What 'L' is a blood-like fluid without red corpuscles?

S: What 'S' is artificial or man-made?

T: What 'T' is to walk heavily or laboriously?

R: What 'R' is a poisonous Australian spider?

C: What 'C' is to ponder?

E: What 'E' is the ejection of an evil spirit?

A: What 'A' is a canvas roof?

V: What 'V' means fox-like?

G: What 'G' is a Libyan leader?

N: What 'N' is someone who constantly scolds?

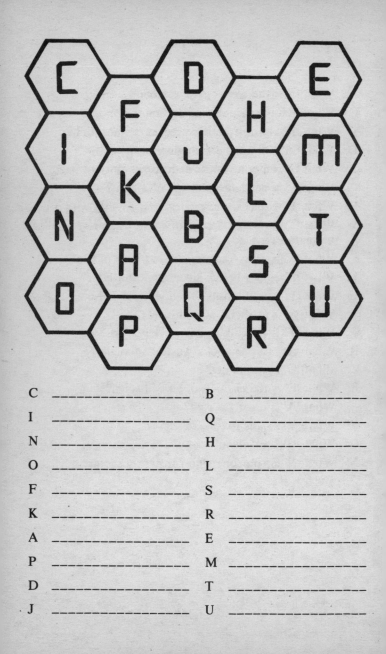

C _____

I _____

N _____

O _____

F _____

K _____

A _____

P _____

D _____

J _____

B _____

Q _____

H _____

L _____

S _____

R _____

E _____

M _____

T _____

U _____

C: What 'C' is the mouth of a volcano?

I: What 'I' is interfamilial sex?

N: What 'N' was first premier of Tanzania?

O: What 'O' is to submit to commands?

F: What 'F' comes after diamond, gold and coal?

K: What 'K' is slang for broken?

A: What 'A' is roused from sleep?

P: What 'P' is an instrument to measure distance walked?

D: What 'D' is the state of owing?

J: What 'J' is to chatter senselessly?

B: What 'B' is the fruit of the *Musa Sapientum*?

Q: What 'Q' means completely – and to a moderate degree?

H: What 'H' is to vacuum?

L: What 'L' is the capital of Peru?

S: What 'S' is slang for an extra-studious type?

R: What 'R' is West Indian pop music?

E: What 'E' is something that supposedly prolongs life?

M: What 'M' is a bivalve mollusc?

T: What 'T' is the sparkle of a star?

U: What 'U' is Northern Ireland?

G	_____	I	_____
Y	_____	L	_____
A	_____	P	_____
T	_____	O	_____
V	_____	H	_____
S	_____	F	_____
U	_____	D	_____
B	_____	M	_____
E	_____	J	_____
N	_____	R	_____

G: What 'G' is a South American cowboy?

Y: What 'Y' is over there?

A: What 'A' is a wide, tree-lined street?

T: What 'T' is a serious bacterium caused disease?

V: What 'V' is a wanderer or tramp?

S: What 'S' is a sweet made with wine and cream?

U: What 'U' means calling for immediate action?

B: What 'B' was the Russian rival of Kruschev?

E: What 'E' is to fraudulently appropriate money?

N: What 'N' is naked?

I: What 'I' is a distinct separate entity?

L: What 'L' is habitual enjoyment of costly things?

P: What 'P' is a Spanish rice dish?

O: What 'O' is a shaft used to propel a boat?

H: What 'H' comes after deer, white and elephant?

F: What 'F' is a species of thrush that winters in Britain?

D: What 'D' are artificial teeth?

M: What 'M' was the Reggae singer who died in 1981?

J: What 'J' is the sidepost of a doorway?

R: What 'R' is India's monetary unit?

C _____
E _____
I _____
N _____
R _____
W _____
D _____
K _____
B _____
V _____

F _____
T _____
S _____
Y _____
L _____
G _____
P _____
U _____
J _____
A _____

C: What 'C' is to assemble or accumulate?

E: What 'E' was the star of *Silver Dream Machine*?

I: What 'I' is to sit on eggs?

N: What 'N' is artless or unsophisticated?

R: What 'R' is to suspend someone from university?

W: What 'W' is a crease in the skin?

D: What 'D' is a person appointed to act for another?

K: What 'K' is an Eastern Inn, a prince and governor?

B: What 'B' is a lure for fish?

V: What 'V' means woundable?

F: What 'F' is an enclosed apparatus for producing heat?

T: What 'T' is a Moroccan free port?

S: What 'S' comes before fish, stick and play?

Y: What 'Y' is a quick tug – and an American?

L: What 'L' is to put to death illegally by mob action?

G: What 'G' was a Japanese movie monster?

P: What 'P' is an earthenware pot – and domestic animal?

U: What 'U' is rising and falling in waves?

J: What 'J' is to cast off a lover?

A: What 'A' was the forbidden fruit?

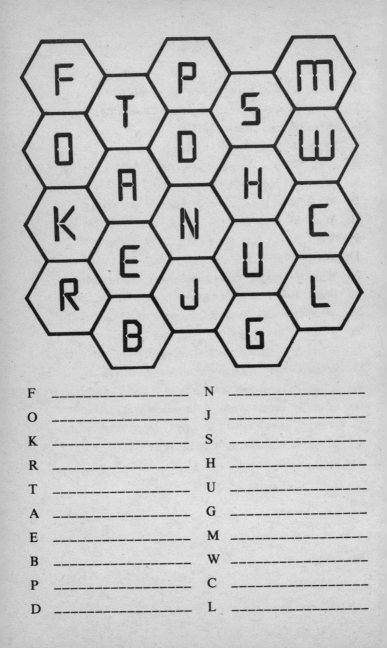

F _____	N _____
O _____	J _____
K _____	S _____
R _____	H _____
T _____	U _____
A _____	G _____
E _____	M _____
B _____	W _____
P _____	C _____
D _____	L _____

F: What 'F' was Prime Minister of Australia?

O: What 'O' is a four-sided pillar terminating in a pyramid?

K: What 'K' is a commotion?

R: What 'R' is a Jamaican sect?

T: What 'T' is a violent hurricane?

A: What 'A' means to do with birds?

E: What 'E' is the festival of Christ's resurrection?

B: What 'B' is to uncover?

P: What 'P' is a universal cure for all ills?

D: What 'D' is a hoist or framework over an oil well?

N: What 'N' comes before front, debt and guard?

J: What 'J' is something said to make you laugh?

S: What 'S' is a long and complex orchestral sonata?

H: What 'H' is emperor of Japan?

U: What 'U' comes before hand, class and cut?

G: What 'G' is thin porridge or near-liquid food?

M: What 'M' is dark and gloomy?

W: What 'W' is a red-brown, stoat-like animal?

C: What 'C' is a kind of revolver?

L: What 'L' is Britain's number two port?

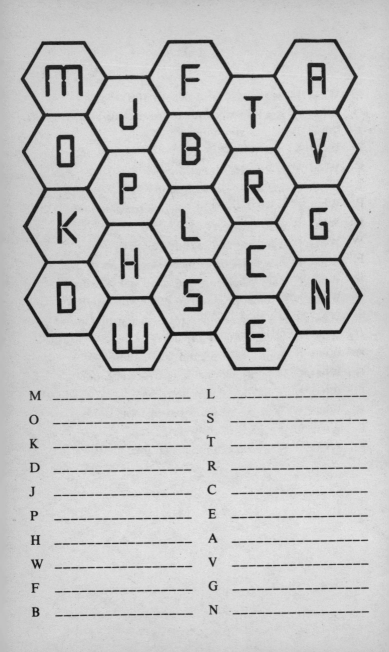

M _____ L _____

O _____ S _____

K _____ T _____

D _____ R _____

J _____ C _____

P _____ E _____

H _____ A _____

W _____ V _____

F _____ G _____

B _____ N _____

M: What 'M' is the nose and mouth of a dog?

O: What 'O' is a musical term for something not to be left out?

K: What 'K' was leader of the USSR?

D: What 'D' is numbered, or proceeding, by tens?

J: What 'J' is someone supposed to bring bad luck?

P: What 'P' is an Italian city famous for ham and cheese?

H: What 'H' is a fence made to be jumped?

W: What 'W' are prevailing atmospheric conditions?

F: What 'F' comes before liquid, ring and tale?

B: What 'B' is to belch?

L: What 'L' is the state secondary school in France?

S: What 'S' are pigs?

T: What 'T' is a business magnate – and a Japanese Shogun?

R: What 'R' is the crossbar in a chair or ladder?

C: What 'C' is small, flat, Indian bread?

E: What 'E' is the opposite of introvert?

A: What 'A' means literally 'messenger'?

V: What 'V' is a Swedish motor car?

G: What 'G' is sea-bird excrement used as fertiliser?

N: What 'N' is the word by which something is known?

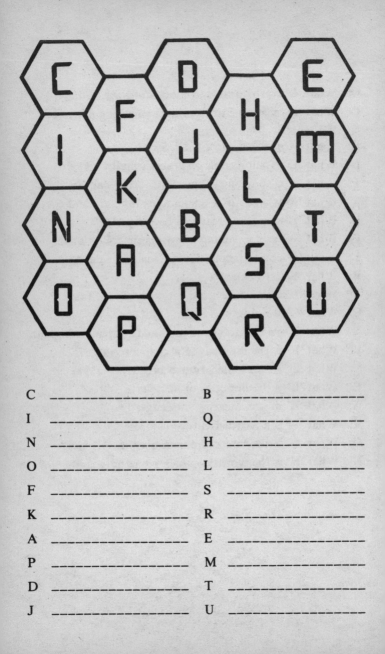

C _____   B _____

I _____   Q _____

N _____   H _____

O _____   L _____

F _____   S _____

K _____   R _____

A _____   E _____

P _____   M _____

D _____   T _____

J _____   U _____

C: What 'C' was the male star of *Educating Rita*?

I: What 'I' is a cast bar of gold or silver?

N: What 'N' is a nursemaid?

O: What 'O' is a notice of someone's death?

F: What 'F' comes before teller, cookie and seeker?

K: What 'K' is a viewing tube containing coloured glass?

A: What 'A' is someone's signature?

P: What 'P' is an Iberian republic?

D: What 'D' is to fail to meet an expectation?

J: What 'J' is a member of the Hebrew people?

B: What 'B' is a curved club, racket stroke – and bow-legged?

Q: What 'Q' is a migratory game bird?

H: What 'H' is a transport aircraft and mythical strongman?

L: What 'L' is true or faithful?

S: What 'S' is the sound of something cutting through air?

R: What 'R' is a brook or gutter?

E: What 'E' is our outer layer of skin?

M: What 'M' is something inexplicable?

T: What 'T' is a bird and a country?

U: What 'U' is to try to persuade?

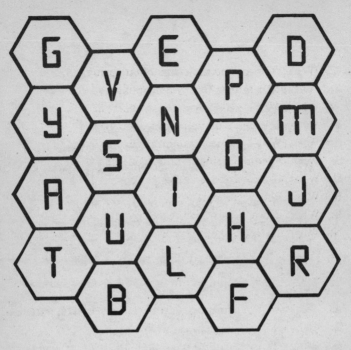

G _____ I _____

Y _____ L _____

A _____ P _____

T _____ O _____

V _____ H _____

S _____ F _____

U _____ D _____

B _____ M _____

E _____ J _____

N _____ R _____

G: What 'G' is an upward gushing hot spring?

Y: What 'Y' is a form of German spoken by Jews?

A: What 'A' is a glass vessel for hypodermic injection?

T: What 'T' is the mountain near Cape Town?

V: What 'V' is a drapery along the edge of a bed?

S: What 'S' comes before board, blade and man?

U: What 'U' was discovered by Herschel in 1781?

B: What 'B' is a bargeman?

E: What 'E' was a jazz pianist and bandleader?

N: What 'N' is thickened petroleum used in incendiary bombs?

I: What 'I' is inebriation?

L: What 'L' is the country with the world's largest merchant fleet?

P: What 'P' is a scaly ant-eater?

O: What 'O' is a fertile place in a desert?

H: What 'H' is the title of the Pope?

F: What 'F' is a small shrill flute?

D: What 'D' is Australia's monetary unit?

M: What 'M' is a genetic alteration?

J: What 'J' was king of the gods?

R: What 'R' is to wrinkle or crumple?

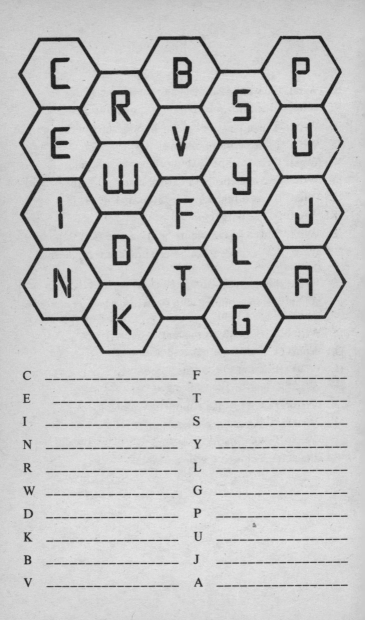

C _____ F _____
E _____ T _____
I _____ S _____
N _____ Y _____
R _____ L _____
W _____ G _____
D _____ P _____
K _____ U _____
B _____ J _____
V _____ A _____

C: What 'C' was the fourth Labour Prime Minister?

E: What 'E' comes before money, song and handed?

I: What 'I' is an angular cut in an edge?

N: What 'N' is the unaided eye?

R: What 'R' is an undersized animal in a litter?

W: What 'W' is a tennis venue?

D: What 'D' is a nightspot to dance in?

K: What 'K' is the holy stone of Islam?

B: What 'B' is a brand of soft drink – and part of a castle's defence?

V: What 'V' is a long (sea) journey?

F: What 'F' was the inventor of the vertical fairground wheel?

T: What 'T' is a plant with brilliant bell-shaped flowers?

S: What 'S' is a Jewish place of worship?

Y: What 'Y' is the Christmas season?

L: What 'L' means growing profusely?

G: What 'G' is the flesh in which teeth stand?

P: What 'P' is to beat by a narrow margin?

U: What 'U' is a mischievous scruffy boy?

J: What 'J' was late 19th century US black music?

A: What 'A' is morbid self-admiration?

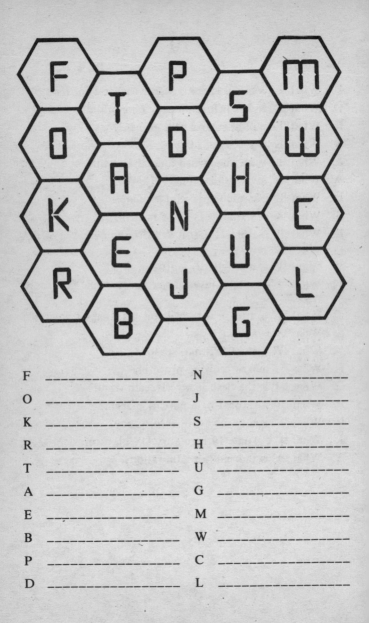

F _____ N _____

O _____ J _____

K _____ S _____

R _____ H _____

T _____ U _____

A _____ G _____

E _____ M _____

B _____ W _____

P _____ C _____

D _____ L _____

F: What 'F' is a ball game played with the hands?

O: What 'O' is to constrain legally or morally?

K: What 'K' is the German munitions dynasty?

R: What 'R' is a cooked mixture of butter and flour?

T: What 'T' is an island off south-east China?

A: What 'A' are all the things you own?

E: What 'E' was the Greek god of love?

B: What 'B' is a voracious West Indian fish?

P: What 'P' is the UK supreme legislature?

D: What 'D' is a ship's crane?

N: What 'N' comes before line, tie and lace?

J: What 'J' is a young kangaroo?

S: What 'S' is to hit at hard and recklessly?

H: What 'H' is the line at which earth and sky seem to meet?

U: What 'U' are the mammary glands of cattle?

G: What 'G' is treachery, deceit or cunning?

M: What 'M' is a plant whose seeds are used as a condiment?

W: What 'W' is a young puppy?

C: What 'C' was the first English printer?

L: What 'L' means pertaining to the moon?

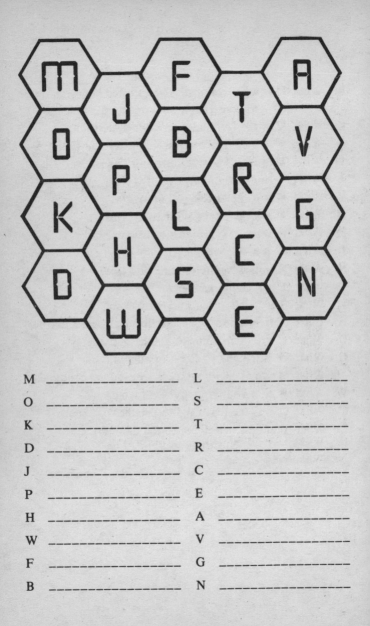

M _____   L _____

O _____   S _____

K _____   T _____

D _____   R _____

J _____   C _____

P _____   E _____

H _____   A _____

W _____   V _____

F _____   G _____

B _____   N _____

M: What 'M' was the detective created by Raymond Chandler?

O: What 'O' is the calling on God as one's witness?

K: What 'K' is something retained as a momento?

D: What 'D' is to dip bread into soup?

J: What 'J' is an island and a jumper?

P: What 'P' is a Spanish cubist painter?

H: What 'H' comes before shot, worm and nose?

W: What 'W' is an Aboriginal spear-throwing stick?

F: What 'F' is a 'modern' ballroom dance?

B: What 'B' is a Moroccan horse, black pigeon and hooked hair?

L: What 'L' was a Russian revolutionary leader?

S: What 'S' is to cheat someone out of their money?

T: What 'T' is a sharp darting pain?

R: What 'R' is to make a thorough search?

C: What 'C' is a living prehistoric fish?

E: What 'E' is to send goods abroad?

A: What 'A' was the province ceded by Germany to France?

V: What 'V' is a contagious poison which causes infection?

G: What 'G' is to dupe or fool someone?

N: What 'N' is a diaper?

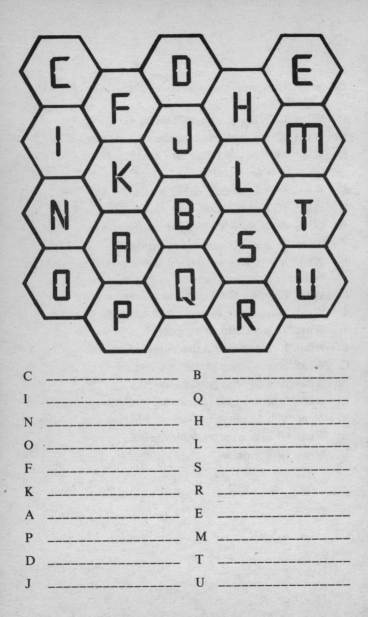

C _____   B _____

I _____   Q _____

N _____   H _____

O _____   L _____

F _____   S _____

K _____   R _____

A _____   E _____

P _____   M _____

D _____   T _____

J _____   U _____

C: What 'C' is a firm of auctioneers?

I: What 'I' is a unit of measure – and a small Scottish island?

N: What 'N' is the back of the neck?

O: What 'O' was the formulator of the law of electric current?

F: What 'F' means tending to split?

K: What 'K' is benevolent?

A: What 'A' is a pear-shaped sub-tropical fruit?

P: What 'P' is a Northern Irish politician?

D: What 'D' is slang for foolish or crazy?

J: What 'J' is a hoarse or discordant noise?

B: What 'B' comes before royal, ship and axe?

Q: What 'Q' is a ring thrown to encircle a peg?

H: What 'H' is an animal supporting a parasite?

L: What 'L' is a guitar-like mediaeval instrument?

S: What 'S' is a landlocked European country?

R: What 'R' is a hernia?

E: What 'E' is to rejoice openly?

M: What 'M' is used as a perfume fixative?

T: What 'T' is a minute pair of tongs?

U: What 'U' is the best of one's abilities?

G _____ I _____

Y _____ L _____

A _____ P _____

T _____ O _____

V _____ H _____

S _____ F _____

U _____ D _____

B _____ M _____

E _____ J _____

N _____ R _____

G: What 'G' was Ronnie Barker's cellmate in *Porridge*?

Y: What 'Y' is a mining territory in North West Canada?

A: What 'A' is to declare invalid?

T: What 'T' comes before spoon, mat and tennis?

V: What 'V' is a large carrion-eating bird?

S: What 'S' is an Italian white wine?

U: What 'U' is a word of hesitation in speech?

B: What 'B' is a wickerwork container?

E: What 'E' was a prince who quit the marines?

N: What 'N' is to relate or recount a story?

I: What 'I' means close in acquaintance?

L: What 'L' is the UK city with thirty-two boroughs?

P: What 'P' is the knob on the hilt of a sword?

O: What 'O' is to preoccupy intensely?

H: What 'H' is the natural home of a species?

F: What 'F' means amusement or enjoyment?

D: What 'D' is a deduction from a price?

M: What 'M' is a soft pulp – or mawkish sentiment?

J: What 'J' was Secretary of State for education?

R: What 'R' is German measles?

C _____   F _____

E _____   T _____

I _____   S _____

N _____   Y _____

R _____   L _____

W _____   G _____

D _____   P _____

K _____   U _____

B _____   J _____

V _____   A _____

C: What 'C' is part of an axle – and an eccentric?

E: What 'E' is a Sicilian volcano?

I: What 'I' is mental insight attained without reasoning?

N: What 'N' means to do with birth?

R: What 'R' comes before stamp, tree and plant?

W: What 'W' is a student at Winchester College?

D: What 'D' is money given as a down payment?

K: What 'K' is a Malay village or enclosed space?

B: What 'B' was a Celtic minstrel or poet?

V: What 'V' was the US Secretary of State who resigned in 1980?

F: What 'F' is an illegal snooker shot?

T: What 'T' is an independent North African state?

S: What 'S' is the trail animals leave behind?

Y: What 'Y' is a unit of currency – and a strong desire?

L: What 'L' is to be hidden in?

G: What 'G' were a TV comedy threesome?

P: What 'P' is an American card game?

U: What 'U' is suave, or smooth, in manner?

J: What 'J' is 'many a true word spoken in'?

A: What 'A' is a non-metric system of weights?

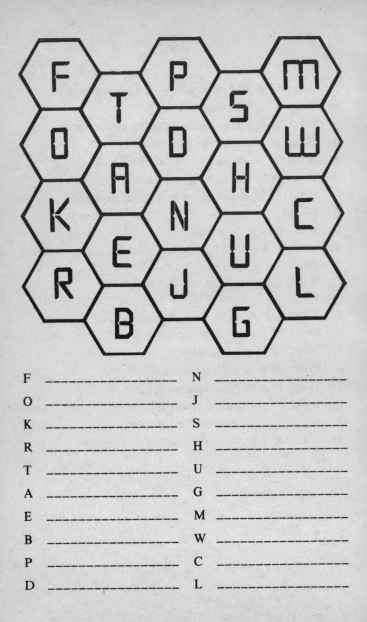

F _____   N _____

O _____   J _____

K _____   S _____

R _____   H _____

T _____   U _____

A _____   G _____

E _____   M _____

B _____   W _____

P _____   C _____

D _____   L _____

F: What 'F' means marked by an otherworldly air?

O: What 'O' is inflexible or stubbornly persistent?

K: What 'K' is a tomato sauce made with vinegar?

R: What 'R' is ready for eating?

T: What 'T' is a ballerina's short, stiff skirt?

A: What 'A' is the Duke of York?

E: What 'E' is to work out something unknown from what is known?

B: What 'B' is a native of Biscay?

P: What 'P' is Adrian Mole's girlfriend?

D: What 'D' is delicately lovely or choice?

N: What 'N' is an Arctic sea-creature with a long straight horn?

J: What 'J' is to poke roughly or stab?

S: What 'S' comes before ball, storm and plough?

H: What 'H' is grey haired with age?

U: What 'U' is a Russian-born film star?

G: What 'G' is a mortar, placed between tiles?

M: What 'M' is to attack with intent to rob?

W: What 'W' is a female member of the navy and a bird?

C: What 'C' is a disease that lasts?

L: What 'L' means wolf-like?

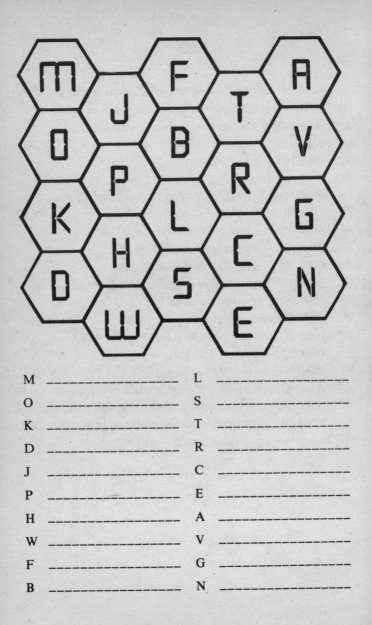

M _____
O _____
K _____
D _____
J _____
P _____
H _____
W _____
F _____
B _____

L _____
S _____
T _____
R _____
C _____
E _____
A _____
V _____
G _____
N _____

M: What 'M' led World War II's most popular band?

O: What 'O' is to hinder or block?

K: What 'K' are the 'Royal Botanic Gardens'?

D: What 'D' is to have a commanding influence over someone?

J: What 'J' was goddess of womanhood?

P: What 'P' is a survey of people's opinion?

H: What 'H' is an otter's lair?

W: What 'W' is a tool to turn nuts and bolts?

F: What 'F' is fancy-free, flirtatious or fickle?

B: What 'B' is a flat-bottomed canal boat?

L: What 'L' was a German protestant reformer?

S: What 'S' is an island republic in South-East Asia?

T: What 'T' is the reverse side of a coin?

R: What 'R' is to do with the country?

C: What 'C' is to twist or wrinkle?

E: What 'E' is a dead volcano or species?

A: What 'A' was the first man on the moon?

V: What 'V' means characteristic of the common people?

G: What 'G' is darkness or despondency?

N: What 'N' comes before shirt, club and light?

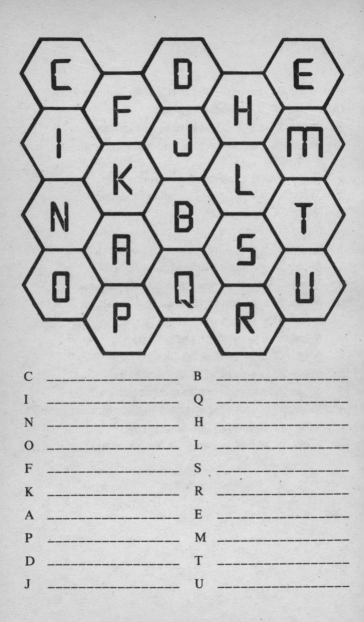

C	_____	B	_____
I	_____	Q	_____
N	_____	H	_____
O	_____	L	_____
F	_____	S	_____
K	_____	R	_____
A	_____	E	_____
P	_____	M	_____
D	_____	T	_____
J	_____	U	_____

C: What 'C' is metal money?

I: What 'I' is to insert at intervals?

N: What 'N' is of little width in proportion to length?

O: What 'O' is dark volcanic rock like bottle glass?

F: What 'F' is a TV games show host?

K: What 'K' is a low island or reef?

A: What 'A' are stress marks over letters?

P: What 'P' is a south Devon seaport?

D: What 'D' is a flat fish – and a pat?

J: What 'J' is a counter with an engraved device?

B: What 'B' is a knife attached to a gun?

Q: What 'Q' is a diamond-shaped pane of glass?

H: What 'H' means goat-like?

L: What 'L' was first Prime Minister of the independent Congo?

S: What 'S' is the righthand side of a boat?

R: What 'R' comes before table, house and head?

E: What 'E' is Ireland?

M: What 'M' is silent or unable to speak?

T: What 'T' is nineteen plus one?

U: What 'U' is a motive and is remote, beyond and in the future?

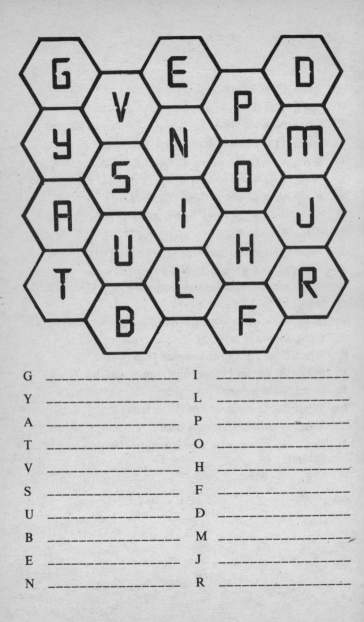

G _____   I _____

Y _____   L _____

A _____   P _____

T _____   O _____

V _____   H _____

S _____   F _____

U _____   D _____

B _____   M _____

E _____   J _____

N _____   R _____

28

G: What 'G' was worth one pound and one shilling?

Y: What 'Y' is a South-West Arabian republic?

A: What 'A' is parched?

T: What 'T' is a Scottish twilled woollen fabric?

V: What 'V' is to hit a ball before it hits the ground?

S: What 'S' is Rin Tin Tin's dog?

U: What 'U' is religious anointing with oil?

B: What 'B' comes before wood, tea and eater?

E: What 'E' was US president from 1953 to 1961?

N: What 'N' is the city at the foot of Mount Vesuvius?

I: What 'I' is underhand plotting?

L: What 'L' are the breathing organs for most vertebrates?

P: What 'P' is to contaminate?

O: What 'O' is a woodwind double reed instrument?

H: What 'H' is the last day of the Scottish year?

F: What 'F' is a bird used in blood sports?

D: What 'D' is a single record?

M: What 'M' is an organ that moves a body part?

J: What 'J' was minister for agriculture?

R: What 'R' was Romulus' legendary co-founder of Rome?

C _____   F _____

E _____   T _____

I _____   S _____

N _____   Y _____

R _____   L _____

W _____   G _____

D _____   P _____

K _____   U _____

B _____   J _____

V _____   A _____

29

C: What 'C' is a Moroccan town – and a Bogart film?

E: What 'E' comes before lark, lid and tooth?

I: What 'I' is communication of disease?

N: What 'N' is a police informer?

R: What 'R' is the singer born Harold Webb?

W: What 'W' is a beaver-like marsupial?

D: What 'D' is an event in the decathlon?

K: What 'K' is the rare gas element Number 36?

B: What 'B' is a ludicrous descent from sublime to commonplace?

V: What 'V' is an Italian volcano?

F: What 'F' comes before gold, mate and errand?

T: What 'T' is a long pointed tooth?

S: What 'S' is a Hindu religious teacher?

Y: What 'Y' was winner of the 1983 John Player League?

L: What 'L' is slang for a drunk?

G: What 'G' was an Apache chieftain?

P: What 'P' is to make glossy by friction?

U: What 'U' is a state of commotion?

J: What 'J' is someone who rides for money?

A: What 'A' is a savoury meat jelly?

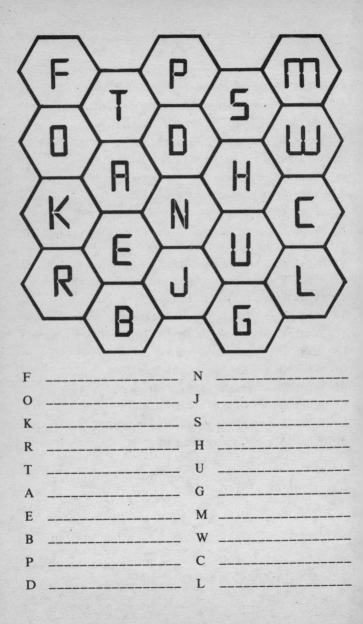

F _____   N _____

O _____   J _____

K _____   S _____

R _____   H _____

T _____   U _____

A _____   G _____

E _____   M _____

B _____   W _____

P _____   C _____

D _____   L _____

30

F: What 'F' is a festival or outdoor bazaar?

O: What 'O' is a rectangle with unequal adjacent sides?

K: What 'K' is a long loose Japanese robe?

R: What 'R' was musical co-writer of *The Sound of Music*?

T: What 'T' is a highnecked sweater?

A: What 'A' is fervour or warm emotion?

E: What 'E' is grossly excessive?

B: What 'B' is a tap on one's privacy and an insect?

P: What 'P' is a place for holding people captive?

D: What 'D' is a mental plan?

N: What 'N' is the kingdom on the southern Himalayas?

J: What 'J' was the Irish author of *Dubliners*?

S: What 'S' comes after lady, friend and lord?

H: What 'H' is a killer drug?

U: What 'U' is portable protection against rain?

G: What 'G' is a coarse or boisterous laugh?

M: What 'M' is a wild American horse?

W: What 'W' is to squirm or roll around in pain?

C: What 'C' was an Egyptian princess?

L: What 'L' is a falconer's apparatus for recalling his hawk?

M _____
O _____
K _____
D _____
J _____
P _____
H _____
W _____
F _____
B _____

L _____
S _____
T _____
R _____
C _____
E _____
A _____
V _____
G _____
N _____

31

M: What 'M' is a fast-growing edible fungus?

O: What 'O' is a bow or gesture expressing submission?

K: What 'K' is approximately 2.2lbs?

D: What 'D' is a TV current affairs presenter?

J: What 'J' is an Israeli orange?

P: What 'P' was the US composer of *High Society*?

H: What 'H' is a game played on ice with a puck?

W: What 'W' is a significant injury to human tissue?

F: What 'F' is a state of excitement – and a table leaf?

B: What 'B' comes after stretcher, message and litter?

L: What 'L' is to make slippery by applying fluid?

S: What 'S' is the world's third most populous city?

T: What 'T' is a sudden involuntary contraction or movement?

R: What 'R' was a Flemish painter?

C: What 'C' is to burn a corpse?

E: What 'E' was Prime Minister after Churchill?

A: What 'A' is unselfish regard for others' welfare?

V: What 'V' is a female fox?

G: What 'G' means of the throat?

N: What 'N' is a substance inducing sleep or stupor?

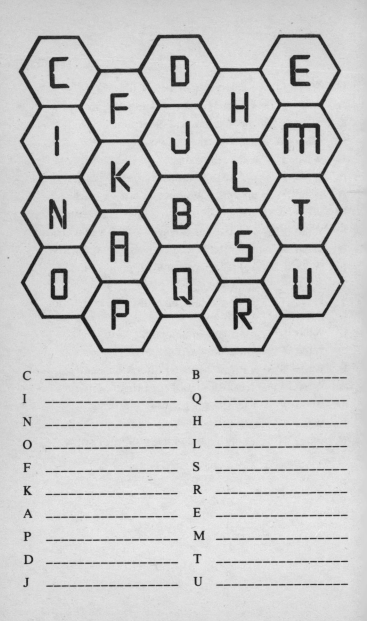

C _____   B _____

I _____   Q _____

N _____   H _____

O _____   L _____

F _____   S _____

K _____   R _____

A _____   E _____

P _____   M _____

D _____   T _____

J _____   U _____

32

C: What 'C' is a caricature or funny illustration?

I: What 'I' is something that cannot be seen?

N: What 'N' is the horse racing capital of England?

O: What 'O' is grossly indecent or repugnant?

F: What 'F' was the saga written by Galsworthy?

K: What 'K' is the dent in the bottom of a bottle?

A: What 'A' is an upper limb of the human body?

P: What 'P' comes before point, money and stripe?

D: What 'D' is the lower few feet of a wall when bordered with wood?

J: What 'J' is Australian slang for sheep?

B: What 'B' are sedative drinks?

Q: What 'Q' was the hunchback of Notre Dame?

H: What 'H' is a continuous record of events?

L: What 'L' is a muscular or rheumatic affliction?

S: What 'S' is a flexible shoot cut from a tree?

R: What 'R' was founder of a banking dynasty?

E: What 'E' is to charm or bewitch?

M: What 'M' is a painting done on a wall?

T: What 'T' is an old-fashioned word for a jailor?

U: What 'U' is an East African country?

G _____	I _____
Y _____	L _____
A _____	P _____
T _____	O _____
V _____	H _____
S _____	F _____
U _____	D _____
B _____	M _____
E _____	J _____
N _____	R _____

33

G: What 'G' is a sound characteristic of pigs?

Y: What 'Y' was the Chinese river now called Chang Jiang?

A: What 'A' is the science of numbers?

T: What 'T' is a small tower?

V: What 'V' is moral excellence or a commendable quality?

S: What 'S' was the British comic actor who died in 1980?

U: What 'U' is a final statement of terms?

B: What 'B' is a boxer who weighs no more than 8st 6lb?

E: What 'E' is a preacher of the Gospel?

N: What 'N' is to persistently provoke someone?

I: What 'I' is a very young child?

L: What 'L' were the 19th century group who wanted to destroy machinery?

P: What 'P' is Ireland's patron saint?

O: What 'O' means pertaining to the eye?

H: What 'H' is rock music with an extra strong beat?

F: What 'F' is a small bet?

D: What 'D' was a surrealist painter?

M: What 'M' comes before box, centre and hall?

J: What 'J' is a sleeved outer garment?

R: What 'R' is an animal that chews the cud?

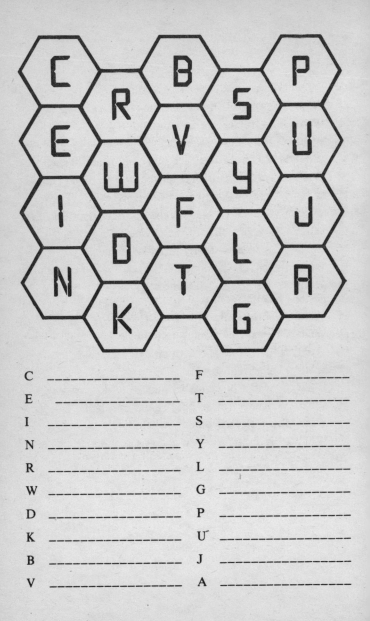

C _____   F _____

E _____   T _____

I _____   S _____

N _____   Y _____

R _____   L _____

W _____   G _____

D _____   P _____

K _____   U _____

B _____   J _____

V _____   A _____

34

C: What 'C' is a withered old woman?

E: What 'E' was an English composer?

I: What 'I' is to fix deeply in the mind?

N: What 'N' is surrounded by West Germany, Belgium and the North Sea?

R: What 'R' is a game like baseball?

W: What 'W' is Australian slang for a killjoy?

D: What 'D' is a large spotted dog?

K: What 'K' are a make of a casual shoe?

B: What 'B' comes after blue, black and goose?

V: What 'V' can be seen?

F: What 'F' is a 'Page 3' pin up and singer?

T: What 'T' is the sound of a plucked guitar string?

S: What 'S' is to move in eddies or whirls?

Y: What 'Y' was the site of a conference between Stalin, Churchill and Roosevelt?

L: What 'L' is a truck?

G: What 'G' is slang for to cheat or swindle?

P: What 'P' was the author of *Doctor Zhivago*?

U: What 'U' is to overturn or knock over?

J: What 'J' is a drinking bout?

A: What 'A' is a type of gazelle and a detergent?

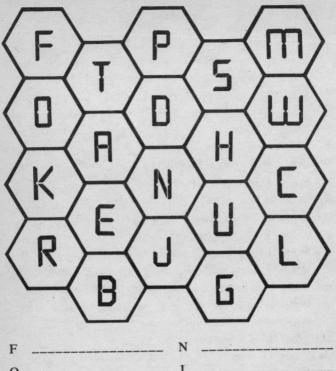

F _____ N _____

O _____ J _____

K _____ S _____

R _____ H _____

T _____ U _____

A _____ G _____

E _____ M _____

B _____ W _____

P _____ C _____

D _____ L _____

35

F: What 'F' means taxation or public revenues?

O: What 'O' is dark or hard to comprehend?

K: What 'K' is a blood relative?

R: What 'R' is an inclined course for skiing?

T: What 'T' comes before writer, face and cast?

A: What 'A' is your signature?

E: What 'E' is an organic catalyst formed by living cells?

B: What 'B' is a pedestal, foundation or base?

P: What 'P' was destroyed by Vesuvius?

D: What 'D' is red-green colour blindness?

N: What 'N' is a community of people within a defined territory?

J: What 'J' is the rock singer born Reginald Dwight?

S: What 'S' is to climb up using hands and feet?

H: What 'H' is deputy leader of the Labour Party?

U: What 'U' was a Nazi submarine?

G: What 'G' is a faster pace than a canter?

M: What 'M' is an East Indian curry soup?

W: What 'W' is verbose?

C: What 'C' was a female whodunnit writer?

L: What 'L' comes before jack, yard and room?

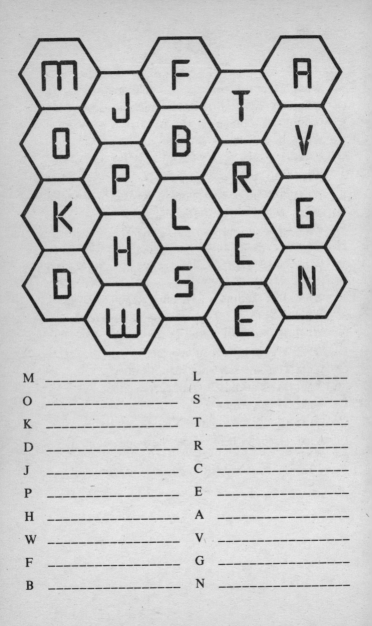

M _____   L _____

O K _____ L S _____

D _____   T _____

J _____   R C _____

P _____   C E _____

H _____   A V _____

W _____   V _____

F _____   G _____

B _____   N _____

36

M: What 'M' comes before racial, millionaire and lingual?

O: What 'O' is the branch of medicine concerned with childbirth?

K: What 'K' is a male sovereign?

D: What 'D' is the heart of the US motor industry?

J: What 'J' is a doleful prophet or denouncer of the times?

P: What 'P' was an English satiric poet?

H: What 'H' is to bargain or wrangle?

W: What 'W' is an invertebrate limbless creeping animal?

F: What 'F' is a sweetheart – and part of a fire?

B: What 'B' is the game played by the Harlem Globe-trotters?

L: What 'L' is a sudden thrust or forward movement?

S: What 'S' was 'The Yorkshire Ripper'?

T: What 'T' is a white-fleshed root plant of the mustard family?

R: What 'R' is rough, disorderly and noisy?

C: What 'C' was a French existentialist novelist?

E: What 'E' is to dig out or unearth?

A: What 'A' was a mythological figure with 100 eyes?

V: What 'V' is ravenous?

G: What 'G' was the folk singer who died in 1967?

N: What 'N' is a toad with a yellow-striped back?

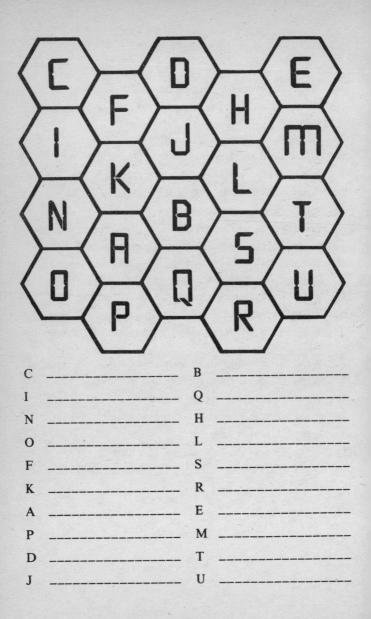

C _____
I _____
N _____
O _____
F _____
K _____
A _____
P _____
D _____
J _____

B _____
Q _____
H _____
L _____
S _____
R _____
E _____
M _____
T _____
U _____

37

C: What 'C' comes before piece, liver and fish?

I: What 'I' means answering to one's highest conception?

N: What 'N' is tidy or undiluted?

O: What 'O' is a building for studying stars?

F: What 'F' is the prevailing custom in dress?

K: What 'K' are glandular organs in the abdominal cavity?

A: What 'A' are periodical county court sessions?

P: What 'P' was Conservative Leader of the House of Commons?

D: What 'D' is a north country valley?

J: What 'J' is slang for talking at length?

B: What 'B' is the noise of hunting dogs?

Q: What 'Q' is a member of the Society of Friends?

H: What 'H' is a burnt offering, or wholesale destruction?

L: What 'L' means the light-bringer?

S: What 'S' is a device to frighten birds?

R: What 'R' is a woman's name – and precious stone?

E: What 'E' is a test of a student's knowledge?

M: What 'M' is a kingdom in north-west Africa?

T: What 'T' is an oleo-resin used to dilute paint?

U: What 'U' is a children's author?

G _____ I _____

Y _____ L _____

A _____ P _____

T _____ O _____

V _____ H _____

S _____ F _____

U _____ D _____

B _____ M _____

E _____ J _____

N _____ R _____

38

G: What 'G' is mean time fixed by?

Y: What 'Y' is a south-east European socialist republic?

A: What 'A' means working by itself?

T: What 'T' is the pale colour between green and blue?

V: What 'V' is empty space or vacuum?

S: What 'S' comes before title, marine and standard?

U: What 'U' is the opposite of downtown?

B: What 'B' is a British heavyweight boxer?

E: What 'E' is a baby eel?

N: What 'N' is a feeling of sickness?

I: What 'I' were the original inhabitants of North America?

L: What 'L' is to sail nearer the wind?

P: What 'P' was the English suffragette?

O: What 'O' is pushy or forward in manner?

H: What 'H' is a long tramp in the country?

F: What 'F' are the limbs a turtle swims with?

D: What 'D' is an indoor game involving pointed missiles?

M: What 'M' is an institution exhibiting objects of interest?

J: What 'J' was the US civil war general nicknamed 'Stonewall'?

R: What 'R' is an animal's tail end?

C _____
E _____
I _____
N _____
R _____
W _____
D _____
K _____
B _____
V _____

F _____
FT _____
S _____
Y _____
L _____
G _____
P _____
U _____
J _____
A _____

39

C: What 'C' is a perforated washing or straining vessel?

E: What 'E' is a high-brow or intellectual?

I: What 'I' is to point out?

N: What 'N' is an ice-cream with different flavoured layers?

R: What 'R' is a pirate, a make of car and a boy scout?

W: What 'W' is the fleece of goat or alpaca?

D: What 'D' was the eldest son of a French king?

K: What 'K' comes before errant, hood and templar?

B: What 'B' is a type of dinosaur?

V: What 'V' is a whirlpool or mass of whirling fluid?

F: What 'F' is the Scottish river 165km long?

T: What 'T' is the total sales revenue of a business?

S: What 'S' is the language of East Africa?

Y: What 'Y' is a rough, idle youth?

L: What 'L' means having full use of one's faculties?

G: What 'G' was the composer of *Porgy and Bess*?

P: What 'P' means multilingual?

U: What 'U' is a horse with a horn on its head?

J: What 'J' was an Empress of France?

A: What 'A' is the act of washing clean?

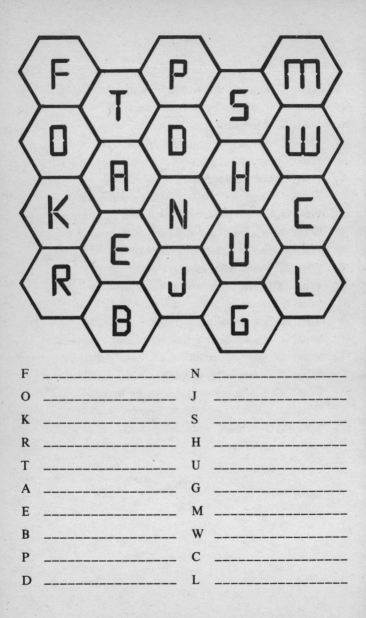

F _____   N _____
O _____   J _____
K _____   S _____
R _____   H _____
T _____   U _____
A _____   G _____
E _____   M _____
B _____   W _____
P _____   C _____
D _____   L _____

40

F: What 'F' is excessive or unnecessarily obsequious?

O: What 'O' is an eight-sided polygon?

K: What 'K' is a rounded protuberance on a door?

R: What 'R' is a Latin American ballroom dance?

T: What 'T' is a US term for dinner jacket?

A: What 'A' is a post-mortem examination?

E: What 'E' means native to a particular place or people?

B: What 'B' is a narrow strip of squared timber?

P: What 'P' was a French psychological novelist?

D: What 'D' was in the TV series *Bonzo and the Rest*?

N: What 'N' is a planet and a sea god?

J: What 'J' is a volcanic Indonesian island?

S: What 'S' comes before fall, coming and circuit?

H: What 'H' is a bleeding disease?

U: What 'U' is a stand-in for theatrical performers?

G: What 'G' is a widely-occurring natural sugar?

M: What 'M' is a maxim adopted as a rule of conduct?

W: What 'W' is a sorceror – and slang for wonderful?

C: What 'C' is to compress into plaits or folds?

L: What 'L' were many French kings?

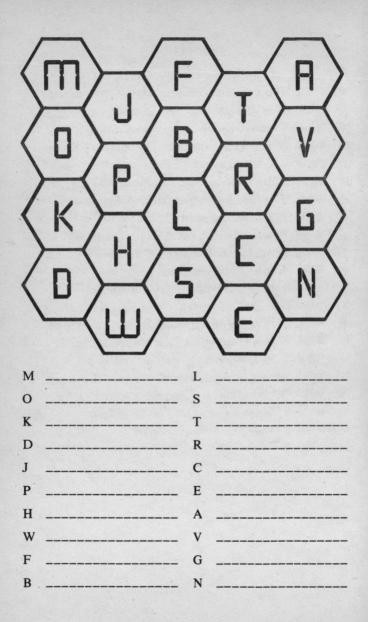

M _____   L _____

O _____   S _____

K _____   T _____

D _____   R _____

J _____   C _____

P _____   E _____

H _____   A _____

W _____   V _____

F _____   G _____

B _____   N _____

41

M: What 'M' is to kill someone unlawfully and intentionally?

O: What 'O' is a South American wild cat?

K: What 'K' comes after Granny, reef and slip?

D: What 'D' was the woman who cut Samson's hair?

J: What 'J' is Australian slang for a novice?

P: What 'P' is an old-fashioned Bohemian dance?

H: What 'H' is obscuration of the atmosphere?

W: What 'W' is an expression of astonishment or admiration?

F: What 'F' means the offspring-bearing sex?

B: What 'B' is the movement of a conductor's baton?

L: What 'L' is a parasitic insect infesting human hair?

S: What 'S' is Britain's fourth largest city?

T: What 'T' is strong string of two or more strands?

R: What 'R' is a spirit distilled from sugar cane?

C: What 'C' comes before hammer, shoulder and cream?

E: What 'E' is the ability to withstand hardship?

A: What 'A' is a writer?

V: What 'V' means of one's own free will?

G: What 'G' is a small pointed beard?

N: What 'N' was independent India's first Prime Minister?

C _____   B _____

I _____   Q _____

N _____   H _____

O _____   L _____

F _____   S _____

K _____   R _____

A _____   E _____

P _____   M _____

D _____   T _____

J _____   U _____

42

C: What 'C' is to wind into rings or spirals?

I: What 'I' is a little devil or mischievous child?

N: What 'N' was President of Egypt before Sadat?

O: What 'O' is to make unnecessary?

F: What 'F' is fustiness of air in a room?

K: What 'K' is a public telephone box?

A: What 'A' means conscious or knowing?

P: What 'P' comes before line, smoker and dream?

D: What 'D' is Australian slang for genuine?

J: What 'J' was the Roman emperor who tried to restore paganism?

B: What 'B' is a bell tower?

Q: What 'Q' was the 'Experiment' in a famour horror film?

H: What 'H' are the long feathers on a pigeon's neck?

L: What 'L' comes before sugar, sum and fish?

S: What 'S' is to make a sudden downward attack?

R: What 'R' is a 17th century broad starched collar?

E: What 'E' is to escape adroitly or evade?

M: What 'M' is a land-locked republic in central Africa?

T: What 'T' is an upper layer of soil bound by grass?

U: What 'U' means a great many?

G _____   I _____

Y _____   L _____

A _____   P _____

T _____   O _____

V _____   H _____

S _____   F _____

U _____   D _____

B _____   M _____

E _____   J _____

N _____   R _____

43

G: What 'G' is an effigy burnt on the 5th November?

Y: What 'Y' comes after solar, church and fiscal?

A: What 'A' is to shrink from with horror?

T: What 'T' is a device for increasing an engine's power?

V: What 'V' is a mouse-like rodent?

S: What 'S' is someone who values property?

U: What 'U' is unpleasing or repulsive to sight?

B: What 'B' is an establishment for the custody of money?

E: What 'E' is an insect with pincers at its rear end?

N: What 'N' was a heroine of the Crimean War?

I: What 'I' is to pass on or communicate?

L: What 'L' is a liquid medicinal preparation used externally?

P: What 'P' are the first settlers in a territory?

O: What 'O' is the 'heads' sign of a coin?

H: What 'H' is the TV cop played by William Shatner?

F: What 'F' was Jung's psychoanalytic teacher?

D: What 'D' is the river that runs through Budapest?

M: What 'M' comes before piece, organ and watering?

J: What 'J' was the first woman to fly solo from England to Australia?

R: What 'R' is to stir up or provoke?

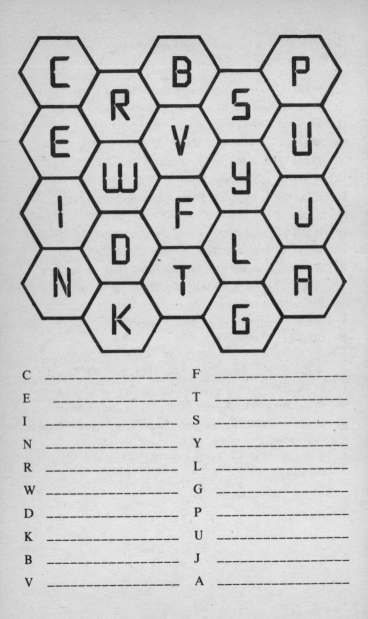

C _____ F _____

E _____ T _____

I _____ S _____

N _____ Y _____

R _____ L _____

W _____ G _____

D _____ P _____

K _____ U _____

B _____ J _____

V _____ A _____

44

C: What 'C' is a tiny Mexican dog?

E: What 'E' is a white Alpine flower?

I: What 'I' is restlessly desirous?

N: What 'N' was a 16th century prophet?

R: What 'R' is a disturbance or noisy commotion?

W: What 'W' means the British governing powers?

D: What 'D' is the Surrey town on the River Mole?

K: What 'K' is a caress given with the lips?

B: What 'B' is a flag, a headline and a symbol of principles?

V: What 'V' is a unit of electromotive force?

F: What 'F' was the star of *The Day of the Jackal*?

T: What 'T' is a US plant rolled about by the wind?

S: What 'S' comes before sonic, market and Ted?

Y: What 'Y' comes before yo and ho?

L: What 'L' is HQ of the MCC?

G: What 'G' is a light white wine – and a burying place?

P: What 'P' are minute spores discharged from the anther of flowers?

U: What 'U' is last or final?

J: What 'J' was the blameless biblical character who suffered endlessly?

A: What 'A' is the centre of an escutcheon – and a bottomless gulf?

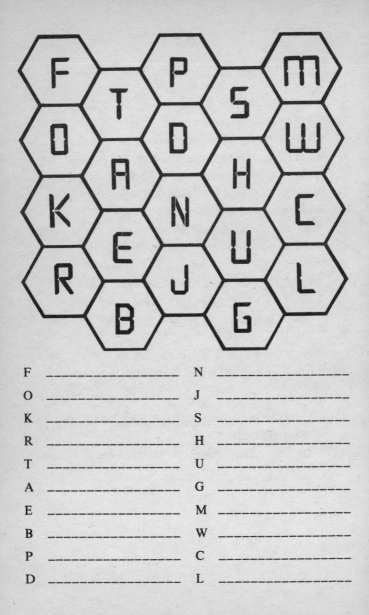

F   ------------------

O   ------------------

K   ------------------

R   ------------------

T   ------------------

A   ------------------

E   ------------------

B   ------------------

P   ------------------

D   ------------------

N   ------------------

J   ------------------

S   ------------------

H   ------------------

U   ------------------

G   ------------------

M   ------------------

W   ------------------

C   ------------------

L   ------------------

45

F: What 'F' is the thighbone?

O: What 'O' means involving the supernatural?

K: What 'K' was the English general who died in 1916?

R: What 'R' is a red cosmetic for the cheeks?

T: What 'T' is a short club or cudgel?

A: What 'A' is to heap up in a mass?

E: What 'E' is a large bird of prey with a hooked bill?

B: What 'B' is a Jersey-based TV series?

P: What 'P' means occurring after death?

D: What 'D' is chairman of the Parliamentary Labour Party?

N: What 'N' was the architect who planned Regent Street?

J: What 'J' is a slatted shutter outside a window?

S: What 'S' is a thick woollen jersey?

H: What 'H' is a pole-mounted trough for carrying bricks?

U: What 'U' comes before marine, mundane and violet?

G: What 'G' is a Swiss cheese full of holes?

M: What 'M' is a contagious disease marked by swelling of the neck?

W: What 'W' is a book that sets up, then solves, a murder mystery?

C: What 'C' is the fourth Zodiacal sign?

L: What 'L' is unevenly balanced or proportional?

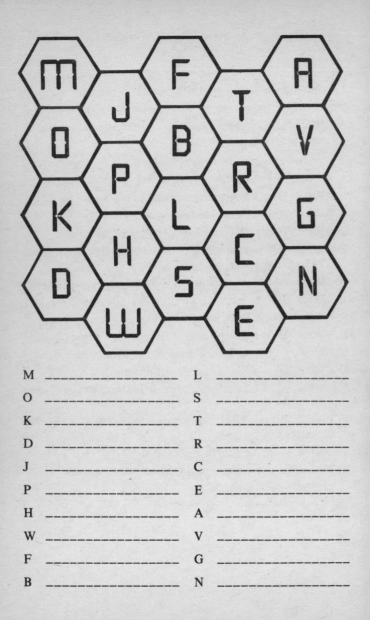

M	_____	L	_____
O	_____	S	_____
K	_____	T	_____
D	_____	R	_____
J	_____	C	_____
P	_____	E	_____
H	_____	A	_____
W	_____	V	_____
F	_____	G	_____
B	_____	N	_____

46

M: What 'M' is the principality between France and Italy?

O: What 'O' is Australia?

K: What 'K' is a small fiddle, wooden tub and personal equipment?

D: What 'D' is the opposite of concord?

J: What 'J' is to squeeze between two surfaces?

P: What 'P' is a small dog with long silky hair?

H: What 'H' is an Australian singer and rapid painter?

W: What 'W' comes before wash, bait and elephant?

F: What 'F' is to go and carry?

B: What 'B' is a round flat cap?

L: What 'L' is the figure produced by string that crosses itself?

S: What 'S' is to drink like a pig?

T: What 'T' is a hard metallic element with a high melting point?

R: What 'R' is a disorderly crowd?

C: What 'C' are the carriers of genes?

E: What 'E' is to set off on a journey?

A: What 'A' was a Greek hero with a bad heel?

V: What 'V' is an animal and comes after field, bank and water?

G: What 'G' is a regiment of Nepalese in the British Army?

N: What 'N' means of the later Stone Age?

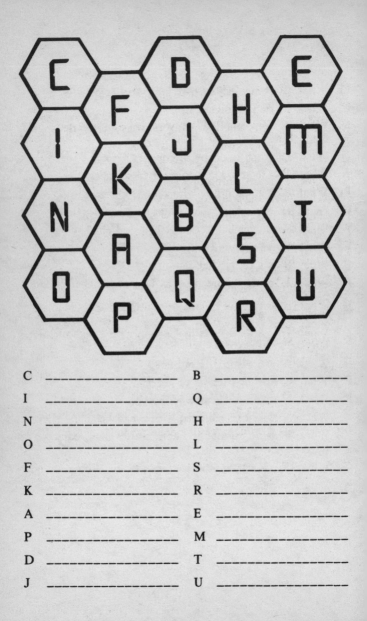

C _____
I _____
N _____
O _____
F _____
K _____
A _____
P _____
D _____
J _____

B _____
Q _____
H _____
L _____
S _____
R _____
E _____
M _____
T _____
U _____

47

C: What 'C' comes before bar, table and bean?

I: What 'I' is an unfairness?

N: What 'N' is a structure made of twigs and feathers?

O: What 'O' is the Australian bush?

F: What 'F' was a British 1950s pop singer?

K: What 'K' is the sound of a funeral bell?

A: What 'A' is the white of an egg?

P: What 'P' is a perfumed ball?

D: What 'D' is the US singer born Robert Zimmerman?

J: What 'J' is a throwing spear?

B: What 'B' means adapted to the use of both eyes?

Q: What 'Q' is to shake or tremble?

H: What 'H' is the full bloom or youth and vigour?

L: What 'L' is talkative?

S: What 'S' comes before tail, hawk and dive?

R: What 'R' is a general report of doubtful accuracy?

E: What 'E' is to lengthen or prolong?

M: What 'M' is the capital of Uruguay?

T: What 'T' is a large game fish related to the mackerel?

U: What 'U' is unmatched or one of a kind?

G —————————	I —————————
Y —————————	L —————————
A —————————	P —————————
T —————————	O —————————
V —————————	H —————————
S —————————	F —————————
U —————————	D —————————
B —————————	M —————————
E —————————	J —————————
N —————————	R —————————

48

G: What 'G' is a French method of execution?

Y: What 'Y' is to be filled with longing?

A: What 'A' is the tree commonly found in wet places?

T: What 'T' is a hard pull – and a type of boat?

V: What 'V' is a ballot?

S: What 'S' is a sample piece of fabric?

U: What 'U' was the counter-culture 1960s art movement?

B: What 'B' comes before hop, ringer and pull?

E: What 'E' is the obscuring of one heavenly body by another?

N: What 'N' means of the nervous system?

I: What 'I' is an alphabetical listing?

L: What 'L' is an old card game and a lavatory?

P: What 'P' is to think over or weigh mentally?

O: What 'O' is a female hormone?

H: What 'H' is a small village – and was a Danish prince?

F: What 'F' is a coniferous tree?

D: What 'D' was New Orleans 1900s jazz?

M: What 'M' is a human body embalmed for burial?

J: What 'J' is a journey for fun?

R: What 'R' are broken fragments of building material?

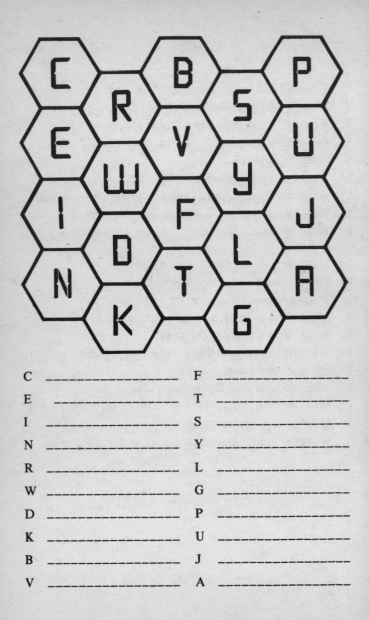

C _____   F _____

E _____   T _____

I _____   S _____

N _____   Y _____

R _____   L _____

W _____   G _____

D _____   P _____

K _____   U _____

B _____   J _____

V _____   A _____

49

C: What 'C' is centigrade?

E: What 'E' is a short trip taken on someone else's business?

I: What 'I' is an oblique hint or allusion?

N: What 'N' is an electrically neutral elementary particle?

R: What 'R' comes before derby, coaster and skate?

W: What 'W' is a gregarious carnivorous quadruped?

D: What 'D' was one of the stars of *Jaws*?

K: What 'K' is a small hill or mound?

B: What 'B' is the front muscle of the upper arm?

V: What 'V' is talkative or fluent in speech?

F: What 'F' is an animal's pelt?

T: What 'T' were the monarchs from Henry VII to Elizabeth I?

S: What 'S' is an absorbent surgical wad?

Y: What 'Y' is a foxhunter's cry?

L: What 'L' comes before shot, hand and jump?

G: What 'G' is a seizing instrument thrown between ships?

P: What 'P' is a British immigrant to Australia?

U: What 'U' is a referee?

J: What 'J' is a variety of zircon – and obscure speech?

A: What 'A' is someone in a bloodthirsty frenzy?

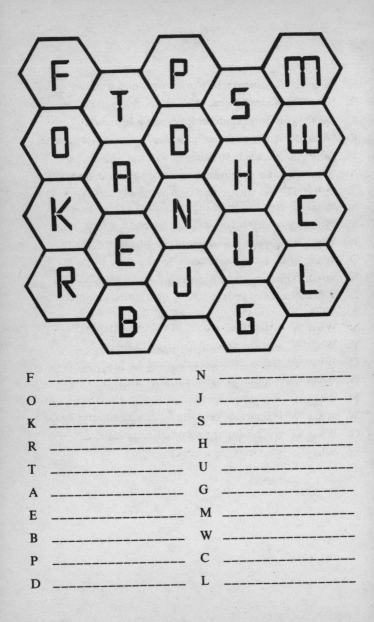

F _____   N _____

O _____   J _____

K _____   S _____

R _____   H _____

T _____   U _____

A _____   G _____

E _____   M _____

B _____   W _____

P _____   C _____

D _____   L _____

50

F: What 'F' is a hearth to work iron – and a showy dress?

O: What 'O' is clearly perceptible?

K: What 'K' is food that complies with Jewish law?

R: What 'R' is the opposite of italics?

T: What 'T' is a local swelling?

A: What 'A' is an appurtenance, an appendix and the wing of a building?

E: What 'E' is a badge of office or flag?

B: What 'B' comes before flop, ache and button?

P: What 'P' is a sea mammal of the whale order?

D: What 'D' is a canine disease – and a type of paint?

N: What 'N' is the upright post in a spiral stair?

J: What 'J' are the people widely distributed in north-west India?

S: What 'S' is the closing of a wound by stitching?

H: What 'H' was the star of *Crocodile Dundee*?

U: What 'U' means present, or occurring, everywhere?

G: What 'G' is sugar in the form of grains?

M: What 'M' is to shed hair or features periodically?

W: What 'W' is the ridge between a horse's shoulder blades?

C: What 'C' is a pit for the disposal of sewage?

L: What 'L' is a sweet on a stick?

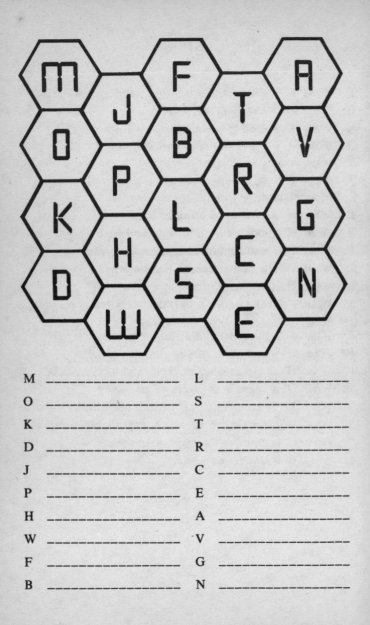

M _____
O _____
K _____
D _____
J _____
P _____
H _____
W _____
F _____
B _____

L _____
S _____
T _____
R _____
C _____
E _____
A _____
V _____
G _____
N _____

51

M: What 'M' is a breakfast dish of dried fruit, oats and nuts?

O: What 'O' means not divisible by two?

K: What 'K' is material for starting a fire?

D: What 'D' is a Rastafarian hair style?

J: What 'J' was the doctor who turned into someone else?

P: What 'P' is a flat-bottomed boat – and a card game?

H: What 'H' was the loser of the Battle of Hastings?

W: What 'W' is to blink deliberately?

F: What 'F' is a feudal term for fidelity to one's lord? `

B: What 'B' is used for baking and also indigestion?

L: What 'L' comes before strife, box and leaf?

S: What 'S' is an additional level of income tax?

T: What 'T' is the London Underground'?

R: What 'R' is a chess piece and a bird?

C: What 'C' means of, or like, deer?

E: What 'E' was temporarily the home of Adam and Eve?

A: What 'A' is a solution, a return hit and a response?

V: What 'V' is a singer?

G: What 'G' is financial assistance from public funds?

N: What 'N' is an old-fashioned word for near?

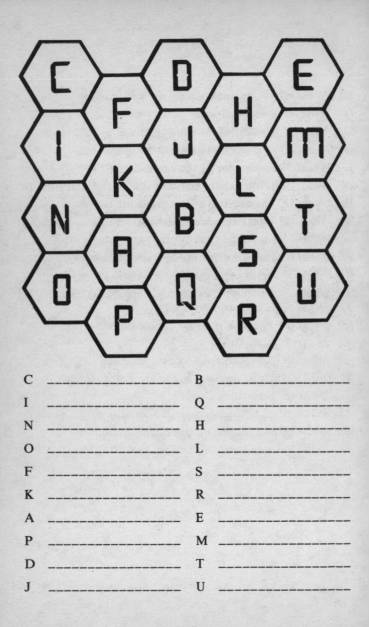

C _____   B _____

I _____   Q _____

N _____   H _____

O _____   L _____

F _____   S _____

K _____   R _____

A _____   E _____

P _____   M _____

D _____   T _____

J _____   U _____

52

C: What 'C' is a raised road across wet ground?

I: What 'I' is to breathe in?

N: What 'N' comes before work, ball and price?

O: What 'O' is general condemnation or hatred?

F: What 'F' was leader of the Third Reich?

K: What 'K' is the Labour Party's home affairs spokesman?

A: What 'A' is a fever in sheep and cattle?

P: What 'P' is an explosive sound, fizzy drink and type of song?

D: What 'D' is submissive or easily managed?

J: What 'J' is a major South African city?

B: What 'B' is a gambling game played on numbered cards?

Q: What 'Q' is a momentary misgiving?

H: What 'H' is a pick, a horse and mediocre writer?

L: What 'L' is an attic?

S: What 'S' is to give oneself up to another?

R: What 'R' is the glancing rebound of a projectile?

E: What 'E' is a Dutch cheese?

M: What 'M' is a building used for worship by Muslems?

T: What 'T' is a Malay word meaning master?

U: What 'U' is in harmony and accord?

G _____ I _____
Y _____ L _____
A _____ P _____
T _____ O _____
V _____ H _____
S _____ F _____
U _____ D _____
B _____ M _____
E _____ J _____
N _____ R _____

53

G: What 'G' comes before scope, plane and tiller?

Y: What 'Y' is a carbon bear?

A: What 'A' is sprinkling – and slander?

T: What 'T' were the emperors of Russia?

V: What 'V' is a magazine and temporary fashion?

S: What 'S' is an excessive amount of something?

U: What 'U' is an Australian term for apartment?

B: What 'B' is to divide into two equal parts?

E: What 'E' is the real or intrinsic nature of something?

N: What 'N' is the opposite of always?

I: What 'I' is a lodging house for travellers?

L: What 'L' comes before smith, jaw and nut?

P: What 'P' is a type of plastic used on foams and moulded products?

O: What 'O' is a wine cask, fencing position and musical intervals?

H: What 'H' is bunkum or theatrical rubbish?

F: What 'F' is to grovel?

D: What 'D' is someone who sleeps on the street?

M: What 'M' is a particle of dust?

J: What 'J' are timbers under floorboards?

R: What 'R' are the eggs of a fish – and a deer?

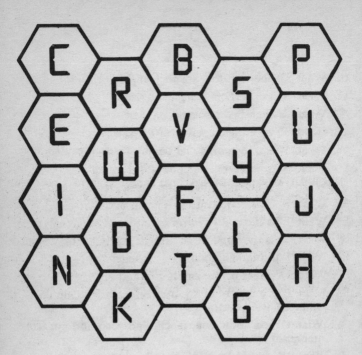

C _____   F _____

E _____   T _____

I _____   S _____

N _____   Y _____

R _____   L _____

W _____   G _____

D _____   P _____

K _____   U _____

B _____   J _____

V _____   A _____

54

C: What 'C' is a natural chamber in the side of a hill?

E: What 'E' is to chose someone by rote?

I: What 'I' means wandering?

N: What 'N' is to take gentle or small bites?

R: What 'R' is the hardening of muscles that occurs after death?

W: What 'W' comes before cord, hand and lash?

D: What 'D' is an identifying label or receipt?

K: What 'K' was a largely prewar US songwriter?

B: What 'B' is that part of the world in which life exists?

V: What 'V' is a credit card and entry permit?

F: What 'F' is the belief that all events are predetermined?

T: What 'T' is a touchdown and an attempt?

S: What 'S' is an Australian river and a bird?

Y: What 'Y' is a volunteer cavalry force raised from countrymen?

L: What 'L' is a weaving machine?

G: What 'G' is a chart expressing a relation between variables?

P: What 'P' is a large steak?

U: What 'U' is uncivilised, awkward or uncultured?

J: What 'J' is to move with a jerk?

A: What 'A' is the science of construction?

F _____   N _____

O _____   J _____

K _____   S _____

R _____   H _____

T _____   U _____

A _____   G _____

E _____   M _____

B _____   W _____

P _____   C _____

D _____   L _____

55

F: What 'F' is an outburst of indignation or fury?

O: What 'O' is a smell?

K: What 'K' is the only truly oceanic gull?

R: What 'R' is a mass for the dead?

T: What 'T' is a card that temporarily outranks another?

A: What 'A' is an orange-coloured fruit allied to the plum?

E: What 'E' is the joint between the fore and upper arm?

B: What 'B' means to camp overnight without tents?

P: What 'P' is the flower opium comes from?

D: What 'D' is a basin with flood gates and a popular weed?

N: What 'N' is petty or persistently annoying?

J: What 'J' is a very large lorry?

S: What 'S' is a conference of top-level politicians?

H: What 'H' is consecrated, sacred or spiritually perfect?

U: What 'U' is a heavy radioactive element?

G: What 'G' is taking place by degrees?

M: What 'M' is a light round bun usually served hot?

W: What 'W' is to make feeble frightened sounds?

C: What 'C' are mounted troops?

L: What 'L' is a large, clawed, marine crustacean?

Solution: Puzzle 1

M: Meringue; O: Offside; K: Kiwi; D: Delta; J: Jolson (Al); P: Punk;
H: Havana; W: Wrath; F: Flag; B: Behead; L: Liszt; S: Suede; T: Two;
R: Rut; C: Chicago; E: Elocution; A: Apollo; V: Verandah; G: Gradient;
N: Noah.

Solution: Puzzle 2

C: Cheltenham; I: Indisposed; N: Nail; O: Omelette; F: Feed; K: Kohl;
A: Azalea; P: Paediatrician; D: Dimmer; J: Janus; B: Butt; Q: Quirk;
H: Hosiery; L: Loch; S: Syringe; R: Rome; E: Ell; M: Mint; T: Train;
U: Uptake.

Solution: Puzzle 3

G: Gulch; Y: Yard; A: Aznavour (Charles); T: Toad; V: Vermouth; S: Syria;
U: Under; B: Bradawl; E: Embassy; N: Nab/Nick; I: Isis; L: Lowe (John);
P: Peking; O: Oscar; H: Heck!; F: Furious; D: Deuce; M: Mutt; J: Jack;
R: Ragtime.

Solution: Puzzle 4

C: Cooper (Gary); E: Electron; I: Incense; N: Newfoundland; R: Roast;
W: Wigwam; D: Dunce; K: Key; B: Baboon; V: Victoria; F: Franco;
T: Tinker; S: Syndicate; Y: Yap; L: Leo; G: Gestation; P: Panama;
U: Unions; J: Joplin; A: Axis.

Solution: Puzzle 5

F: Fitzgerald (Ella); O: Offset; K: Koala; R: Rough; T: Toledo; A: Axiom;
E: Eastwood (Clint); B: Balcony; P: Pray; D: Drip; N: New; J: Jamboree;
S: Synopsis/Summary; H: Harry; U: United; G: Gruff; M: Maori;
W: Wallet; C: Coax; L: Late!

Solution: Puzzle 6

M: Marvin (Lee); O: Oasthouse; K: Kale; D: Dally; J: Jaundice; P: Piraeus;
H: Harrison; W: Wallaby; F: Folk; B: Ballesteros; L: Litter; S: Syrup;
T: Tartar; R: Rustle; C: Cobra; E: Elope; A: Awhile; V: Vow; G: Grub;
N: Nadir.

Solution: Puzzle 7

C: Cock; I: Iglesias; N: Nick; O: Oink; F: Fettle; K: Krugerrand; A: Awash; P: Porcupine; D: Democracy; J: Jig; B: Banal; Q: Quant (Mary); H: Hunk; L: Laos; S: Synod; R: Ruthless; E: Elide; M: Mutton; T: Tasmania; U: Umbrage.

Solution: Puzzle 8

G: Glasgow; Y: Yacht; A: Avuncular; T: Twiddle; V: Virgo; S: Savile (Jimmy); U: Ulcer; B: Bag; E: Excited; N: Naafi; I: Inception; L: Larrikan; P: Prom; O: Obese; H: Heseltine (Michael); F: Forceps; D: Dairy; M: Motown; J: Junoesque; R: Rusk.

Solution: Puzzle 9

C: Cardin; E: Element; I: Incur; N: Nap; R: Rye; W: Wapping; D: Donor; K: Ken; B: Ballot; V: Vulcan; F: Ford; T: Twit/Twerp; S: Symbiosis; Y: Yokohama; L: Lurch; G: Grouse; P: Portfolio; U: Utopia; J: Jigger; A: Awkward.

Solution: Puzzle 10

F: Ferric/Ferrous; O: Ocean (Billy); K: Kayak; R: Rush; T: Tibet; A: Aries; E: Ember; B: Bank; P: Port; D: Domestic; N: Nacelle; J: Juvenal; S: Swizzle; H: Humdrum; U: Unemployed; G: Guitar; M: Myth; W: Weaver; C: Culpable; L: Lairy.

Solution: Puzzle 11

M: Multiply; O: Osmonds; K: Kapok; D: Derbyshire/Durham; J: Jeroboam; P: Port; H: Humble; W: Wetbacks; F: Falstaff; B: Back; L: Lymph; S: Synthetic; T: Trudge; R: Redback; C: Cogitate; E: Exorcism; A: Awning; V: Vulpine; G: Gaddafi; N: Nag.

Solution: Puzzle 12

C: Crater; I: Incest; N: Nyerere; O: Obey; F: Field; K: Kaput; A: Awakened; P: Pedometer; D: Debt; J: Jabber; B: Banana; Q: Quite; H: Hoover; L: Lima; S: Swot; R: Reggae; E: Elixir; M: Mussel; T: Twinkle; U: Ulster.

Solution: Puzzle 13

G: Gaucho; Y: Yonder; A: Avenue; T: Typhoid; V: Vagabond; S: Syllabub; U: Urgent; B: Bulgarin; E: Embezzle; N: Nude; I: Individual; L: Luxury; P: Paella; O: Oar; H: Hunter; F: Fieldfare; D: Dentures; M: Marley; J: Jamb; R: Rupee.

Solution: Puzzle 14

C: Collect; E: Essex (David); I: Incubate; N: Naive; R: Rusticate; W: Wrinkle; D: Deputy; K: Khan; B: Bait; V: Vulnerable; F: Furnace; T: Tangier; S: Sword; Y: Yank; L: Lynch; G: Godzilla; P: Pig; U: Undulating; J: Jilt; A: Apple.

Solution: Puzzle 15

F: Fraser; O: Obelisk; K: Kerfuffle; R: Rastafarian; T: Typhoon; A: Avian; E: Easter; B: Bare; P: Panacea; D: Derrick; N: National; J: Joke; S: Symphony; H: Herohito; U: Upper; G: Gruel; M: Murky; W: Weasel; C: Colt; L: Liverpool.

Solution: Puzzle 16

M: Muzzle; O: Obligate; K: Khrushchev; D: Decimal; J: Jinx/Jonah; P: Parma; H: Hurdle; W: Weather; F: Fairy; B: Burp; L: Lycée; S: Swine; T: Tycoon; R: Rung; C: Chupatty; E: Extrovert; A: Apostle; V: Volvo; G: Guano; N: Name.

Solution: Puzzle 17

C: Caine (Michael); I: Ingot; N: Nanny; O: Obituary; F: Fortune; K: Kaleidoscope; A: Autograph; P: Portugal; D: Disappoint; J: Jew; B: Bandy; Q: Quail; H: Hercules; L: Loyal; S: Swish; R: Runnel; E: Epidermis; M: Mystery; T: Turkey; U: Urge.

Solution: Puzzle 18

G: Geyser; Y: Yiddish; A: Ampoule; T: Table: V: Valance; S: Switch; U: Uranus; B: Bargee; E: Ellington (Duke); N: Napalm; I: Intoxication; L: Liberia; P: Pangolin; O: Oasis; H: Holiness; F: Fife; D: Dollar; M: Mutation; J: Jupiter; R: Rumple.

Solution: Puzzle 19

C: Callaghan; E: Even; I: Indentation; N: Naked; R: Runt; W: Wimbledon; D: Disco; K: Kaaba; B: Barbican; V: Voyage; F: Ferris; T: Tulip; S: Synagogue; Y: Yuletide; L: Luxuriant; G: Gums; P: Pip; U: Urchin; J: Jazz; A: Autism.

Solution: Puzzle 20

F: Fives; O: Obligate; K: Krupp; R: Roux; T: Taiwan; A: Assets; E: Eros; B: Barracuda; P: Parliament; D: Davit; N: Neck; J: Joey; S: Swipe; H: Horizon; U: Udder; G: Guile; M: Mustard; W: Whelp; C: Caxton; L: Lunar.

Solution: Puzzle 21

M: Marlowe; O: Oath; K: Keepsake; D: Dunk; J: Jersey; P: Picasso; H: Hook; W: Woomera; F: Foxtrot; B: Barb; L: Lenin; S: Swindle; T: Twinge; R: Rummage; C: Coelacanth; E: Export; A: Alsace; V: Virus; G: Gull; N: Nappy.

Solution: Puzzle 22

C: Christie; I: Inch; N: Nape; O: Ohm; F: Fissile; K: Kind; A: Avocado; P: Paisley; D: Daft; J: Jangle; B: Bathe; Q: Quoit; H: Host; L: Lute/Lyre; S: Switzerland; R: Rupture; E: Exult; M: Musk; T: Tweezers; U: Utmost.

Solution: Puzzle 23

G: Godber; Y: Yukon; A: Annul; T: Table; V: Vulture; S: Soave; U: Um; B: Basket; E: Edward; N: Narrate; I: Intimate; L: London; P: Pommel; O: Obsess; H: Habitat; F: Fun; D: Discount; M: Mush; J: Jospeh (Keith); R: Rubella.

Solution: Puzzle 24

C: Crank; E: Etna; I: Intuition; N: Natal; R: Rubber; W: Wykehamist; D: Deposit; K: Kampong; B: Bard; V: Vance; F: Foul; T: Tunisia; S: Spoor; Y: Yen; L: Lurk; G: Goodies; P: Poker; U: Urban; J: Jest; A: Avoirdupois.

Solution: Puzzle 25

F: Fey; O: Obdurate; K: Ketchup; R: Ripe; T: Tutu; A: Andrew; E: Extrapolate; B: Basque; P: Pandora; D: Dainty; N: Narwhal; J: Jab; S: Snow; H: Hoar; U: Ustinov (Peter); G: Grout; M: Mug; W: Wren; C: Chronic; L: Lupine.

Solution: Puzzle 26

M: Miller; O: Obstruct; K: Kew; D: Dominate; J: Juno; P: Poll; H: Holt; W: Wrench; F: Flighty; B: Barge; L: Luther; S: Singapore; T: Tails; R: Rural/Rustic; C: Crinkle; E: Extinct; A: Armstrong; V: Vulgar; G: Gloom; N: Night.

Solution: Puzzle 27

C: Coin; I: Intersperse; N: Narrow; O: Obsidian; F: Forsythe (Bruce); K: Key; A: Accents; P: Plymouth; D: Dab; J: Jetton; B: Bayonet; Q: Quarrel; H: Hircine; L: Lumumba; S: Starboard; R: Round; E: Eire; M: Mute; T: Twenty; U: Ulterior.

Solution: Puzzle 28

G: Guinea; Y: Yemen; A: Arid; T: Tweed; V: Volley; S: Snowy; U: Unction; B: Beef; E: Eisenhower; N: Naples; I: Intrigue; L: Lungs; P: Pollute; O: Oboe; H: Hogmanay; F: Falcon; D: Disc; M: Muscle; J: Jopling; R: Remus.

Solution: Puzzle 29

C: Casablanca; E: Eye; I: Infection; N: Nark; R: Richard (Cliff); W: Wombat; D: Discus; K: Krypton; B: Bathos; V: Vesuvius; F: Fool's; T: Tusk; S: Swami; Y: Yorkshire; L: Lush; G: Geronimo; P: Polish; U: Uproar; J: Jockey; A: Aspic.

Solution: Puzzle 30

F: Fête; O: Oblong; K: Kimono; R: Rodgers; T: Turtleneck; A: Arduous; E: Exorbitant; B: Bug; P: Prison; D: Design; N: Nepal; J: Joyce; S: Ship; H: Heroin; U: Umbrella; G: Guffaw; M: Mustang; W: Writhe; C: Cleopatra; L: Lure.

Solution: Puzzle 31

M: Mushroom; O: Obeisance; K: Kilogram; D: Dimbleby (David); J: Jaffa;
P: Porter; H: Hockey; W: Wound; F: Flap; B: Bearer; L: Lubricate;
S: Shanghai; T: Twitch; R: Rubens; C: Cremate; E: Eden (Anthony);
A: Altruism; V: Vixen; G: Gutteral; N: Narcotic.

Solution: Puzzle 32

C: Cartoon; I: Invisible; N: Newmarket; O: Obscene; F: Forsyte; K: Kick;
A: Arm; P: Pin; D: Dado; J: Jumpbuck; B: Barbiturates; Q: Quasimodo;
H: History; L: Lumbago; S: Switch; R: Rothschild; E: Enchant; M: Mural;
T: Turnkey; U: Uganda.

Solution: Puzzle 33

G: Grunt; Y: Yangtze; A: Arithmetic; T: Turret; V: Virtue; S: Sellers (Peter);
U: Ultimatum; B: Bantamweight; E: Evangelist; N: Needle; I: Infant;
L: Luddites; P: Patrick; O: Ocular; H: Hard; F: Flutter; D: Dali (Salvador);
M: Music; J: Jacket; R: Ruminant.

Solution: Puzzle 34

C: Crone; E: Elgar; I: Impress; N: Netherlands; R: Rounders; W: Wowser;
D: Dalmatian; K: Kickers; B: Berry; V: Visible; F: Fox (Samantha);
T: Twang; S: Swirl; Y: Yalta; L: Lorry; G: Gyp; P: Pasternak (Boris);
U: Upset/Upturn; J: Jug; A: Ariel.

Solution: Puzzle 35

F: Fiscal; O: Obscure; K: Kin; R: Run; T: Type; A: Autograph; E: Enzyme;
B: Basis; P: Pompeii; D: Daltonism; N: Nation; J: John (Elton); S: Swarm;
H: Hattersley; U: U-Boat; G: Gallop; M: Mulligatawny; W: Wordy;
C: Christie (Agatha); L: Lumber.

Solution: Puzzle 36

M: Multi; O: Obstetrics; K: King; D: Detroit; J: Jeremiah; P: Pope;
H: Haggle; W: Worm; F: Flame; B: Basketball; L: Lunge; S: Sutcliffe
(Peter); T: Turnip; R: Rowdy; C: Camus; E: Excavate; A: Argus;
V: Voracious; G: Guthrie (Arlo); N: Natterjack.

Solution: Puzzle 37

C: Cod; I: Ideal; N: Neat; O: Observatory; F: Fashion;. K: Kidneys;
A: Assizes; P: Prior/Pym; D: Dale; J: Jaw; B: Baying; Q: Quaker;
H: Holocaust; L: Lucifer; S: Scarecrow; R: Ruby; E: Examination;
M: Morocco; T: Turpentine; U: Utley (Alison).

Solution: Puzzle 38

G: Greenwich; Y: Yugoslavia; A: Automatic; T: Turquoise; V: Void; S: Sub;
U: Uptown; B: Bruno (Frank); E: Elver; N: Nausea; I: Indians; L: Luff;
P: Pankhurst (Emily); O: Obtrusive; H: Hike; F: Flippers; D: Darts;
M: Museum; J: Jackson; R: Rump.

Solution: Puzzle 39

C: Colander; E: Egghead; I: Indicate; N: Neapolitan; R: Rover; W: Wool;
D: Dauphin; K: Knight; B: Brontosaurus; V: Vortex; F: Forth; T: Turnover;
S: Swahili; Y: Yobbo/Yob; L: Lucid; G: Gershwin; P: Polyglot; U: Unicorn;
J: Josephine; A: Ablutions.

Solution: Puzzle 40

F: Fulsome; O: Octagon; K: Knob; R: Rumba; T: Tuxedo; A: Autopsy;
E: Endemic; B: Batten; P: Proust; D: Dodger; N: Neptune; J: Java; S: Short;
H: Haemophilia; U: Understudy; G: Glucose; M: Motto; W: Wizard;
C: Crimp; L: Louis.

Solution: Puzzle 41

M: Murder; O: Ocelot; K: Knot; D: Delilah; J: Jackaroo; P: Polka; H: Haze;
W: Wow!; F: Female; B: Beat; L: Louse; S: Sheffield; T: Twine; R: Rum;
C: Cold; E: Endurance; A: Author; V: Voluntary; G: Goatee; N: Nehru.

Solution: Puzzle 42

C: Coil; I: Imp; N: Nasser; O: Obviate; F: Fug; K: Kiosk; A: Aware;
P: Pipe; D: Dinkum; J: Julian; B: Belfry; Q: Quatermass; H: Hackles;
L: Lump; S: Swoop; R: Ruff; E: Elude; M: Malawi; T: Turf; U: Umpteen.

Solution: Puzzle 43

G: Guy; Y: Year; A: Abhor; T: Turbocharger; V: Vole; S: Surveyor; U: Ugly; B: Bank; E: Earwig; N: Nightingale; I: Impart; L: Lotion; P: Pioneers; O: Observe; H: Hooker; F: Freud; D: Danube; M: Mouth; J: Johnson (Amy); R: Rouse.

Solution: Puzzle 44

C: Chihuahua; E: Edelweiss; I: Impatient; N: Nostradamus; R: Rumpus/Row; W: Whitehall; D: Dorking; K: Kiss; B: Banner; V: Volt; F: Fox (Edward); T: Tumbleweed; S: Super; Y: Yo; L: Lords; G: Graves; P: Pollen; U: Ultimate; J: Job; A: Abyss.

Solution: Puzzle 45

F: Femur; O: Occult; K: Kitchener; R: Rouge; T: Truncheon; A: Accumulate; E: Eagle; B: Bergerac; P: Posthumous; D: Dormand; N: Nash; J: Jalousie; S: Sweater; H: Hod; U: Ultra; G: Gruyère; M: Mumps; W: Whodunnit; C: Cancer; L: Lopsided.

Solution: Puzzle 46

M: Monaco; O: Oz; K: Kit; D: Discord; J: Jam; P: Pomeranian/Pekinese; H: Harris (Rolf); W: White; F: Fetch; B: Beret; L: Loop; S: Swill; T: Tungstun; R: Rabble; C: Chromosomes; E: Embark; A: Achilles; V: Vole; G: Gurkha; N: Neolithic.

Solution: Puzzle 47

C: Coffee; I: Injustice; N: Nest; O: Outback; F: Fury (Billy); K: Knell; A: Albumen; P: Pomander; D: Dylan (Bob); J: Javelin; B: Binocular; Q: Quake; H: Heyday; L: Loquacious; S: Swallow; R: Rumour; E: Elongate; M: Montevideo; T: Tuna; U: Unique.

Solution: Puzzle 48

G: Guillotine; Y: Yearn; A: Alder; T: Tug; V: Vote; S: Swatch; U: Underground; B: Bell; E: Eclipse; N: Neural; I: Index; L: Loo; P: Ponder; O: Oestrogen; H: Hamlet; F: Fir; D: Dixieland; M: Mummy; J: Jaunt; R: Rubble.

Solution: Puzzle 49

C: Celsius; E: Errand; I: Innuendo; N: Neutron; R: Roller; W: Wolf; D: Dreyfus (Richard); K: Knoll; B: Biceps; V: Voluble; F: Fur; T: Tudor; S: Swab; Y: Yoicks; L: Long; G: Grapnel; P: Pommy; U: Umpire; J: Jargon; A: Amok.

Solution: Puzzle 50

F: Finery; O: Obvious; K: Kosher; R: Roman; T: Tumour; A: Annex; E: Ensign; B: Belly; P: Porpoise; D: Distemper; N: Newel; J: Jats; S: Suture; H: Hogan (Paul); U: Universal; G: Granulated; M: Moult; W: Withers; C: Cesspit; L: Lollipop.

Solution: Puzzle 51

M: Muesli; O: Odd; K: Kindling; D: Dreadlock; J: Jekyll; P: Pontoon; H: Harold; W: Wink; F: Fealty; B: Bicarbonate; L: Loose; S: Surtax; T: Tube; R: Rook; C: Cervine; E: Eden; A: Answer; V: Vocalist; G: Grant; N: Nigh.

Solution: Puzzle 52

C: Causeway; I: Inhale; N: Net; O: Odium; F: Führer; K: Kaufman; A: Anthrax; P: Pop; D: Docile; J: Johannesburg; B: Bingo; Q: Qualm; H: Hack; L: Loft; S: Surrender; R: Ricochet; E: Edam; M: Mosque; T: Tuan; U: Unison/Unity.

Solution: Puzzle 53

G: Gyro; Y: Yogi; A: Aspersion; T: Tzars; V: Vogue; S: Surfeit; U: Unit; B: Bisect; E: Essence; N: Never; I: Inn; L: Lock; P: Polystyrene; O: Octave; H: Hokum; F: Fawn; D: Dosser; M: Mote; J: Joists; R: Roe.

Solution: Puzzle 54

C: Cave; E: Elect; I: Itinerant; N: Nibble; R: Rigormortis; W: Whip; D: Docket; K: Kern; B: Biosphere; V: Visa; F: Fatalism; T: Try; S: Swan; Y: Yeomanry; L: Loom; G: Graph; P: Porterhouse; U: Uncouth; J: Jolt; A: Architecture.

Solution: Puzzle 55

F: Furore; O: Odour; K: Kittiwake; R: Requiem; T: Trump; A: Apricot;
E: Elbow; B: Bivouac; P: Poppy; D: Dock; N: Niggling; J: Juggernaut;
S: Summit; H: Holy; U: Uranium; G: Gradual; M: Muffin; W: Whimper;
C: Cavalry; L: Lobster.

The Freakiest, Funniest Book About Animals – *Ever!*

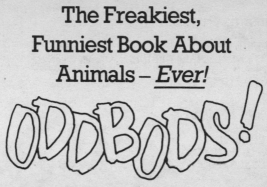

Bill Garnett

FIRST THERE WAS *THE NAKED APE*. THEN CAME *THE NAKED NUN*... NOW – AT LAST – THE NAKED TRUTH!

There are creatures that walk this planet which:

* *Bathe in acid*
* *Baffle Radar*
* *Turn into plants*
* *Do business – and have sex – without their heads*

You'll find them – and many others even stranger – in *ODDBODS!*

IT'S EVERYTHING YOU NEVER WANTED TO KNOW ABOUT ANIMALS – BUT WILL BE STAGGERED TO HEAR!

HUMOUR/NON-FICTION   0 7221 3809 1   £1.75